Miracle Cure

How to Solve America's Health Care Crisis and Why Canada Isn't the Answer

Miracle Cure

How to Solve America's Health Care Crisis and Why Canada Isn't the Answer

By Sally C. Pipes

With a foreword by Milton Friedman

Pacific Research Institute
San Francisco
California

The Fraser Institute
Vancouver, Calgary, Toronto
Canada

Printed and bound in Canada.

Library and Archives Canada Cataloguing in Publication

Pipes, Sally, 1945-

    Miracle cure : how to solve America's health care crisis and why Canada isn't the answer / by Sally C. Pipes ; with a foreword by Milton Friedman.

Includes bibliographical references.
ISBN 0-936488-92-1 (Pacific Research Institute).—
ISBN 0-88975-212-5 (Fraser Institute)

    1. Health care reform—United States. 2. Health care reform—Canada. I. Fraser Institute (Vancouver, B.C.) II. Pacific Research Institute for Public Policy III. Title.

RA395.N7P56 2004   362.1'0973   C2004-905096-6

Table of Contents

Part Two
The Canadian Solution: Legalize Competition

ACKNOWLEDGEMENTS

I would like to thank the following individuals for their contributions to this book: Naomi Lopez Bauman, Mark Davis, and Christopher Middleton. I thank Dr. David Gratzer, senior fellow at the Manhattan Institute, for his invaluable suggestions. I also thank those scholars and health care experts who served as peer reviewers and the many other free-market think tanks that have encouraged and contributed to PRI's work in this area.

I am especially grateful to my friend and mentor Milton Friedman for writing the foreword to this book and for his invaluable suggestions on how to improve it. And I thank Michael Walker, executive director of The Fraser Institute, and his staff for co-publishing the book and for providing guidance and support along the way.

Very special thanks also go to the contributors to the Pacific Research Institute, who made my work on this project possible. I am tremendously appreciative of your intellectual, as well as monetary, support.

Any errors or omissions are my sole responsibility.

—*Sally C. Pipes*

ABOUT THE AUTHOR

Sally C. Pipes is president and chief executive officer of the Pacific Research Institute, a San Francisco-based think tank founded in 1979. Prior to becoming president in 1991, she was assistant director of The Fraser Institute, based in Vancouver, Canada.

Ms. Pipes addresses national and international audiences on health care, women's issues, education, privatization, civil rights, and the economy. She has been interviewed on CNNfn, "20/20," "The Today Show," "Dateline," "The Dennis Miller Show," and other prominent programs.

She has written regular columns for *Chief Executive, Investor's Business Daily*, and the *San Francisco Examiner*. Her opinion pieces have appeared in the *Washington Post, Financial Times of London, New York Times, Los Angeles Times, San Francisco Examiner, San Francisco Chronicle, Sacramento Bee,* and *Orange County Register*. She also co-authored with Spencer Star *Income and Taxation in Canada* and co-authored with Michael Walker seven editions of *Tax Facts*.

A Canadian residing in the United States, Ms. Pipes writes, speaks, and gives invited testimony at the national and state levels on key health care issues facing America. Topics have included the false promise of a single-payer system as exists in Canada, pharmaceutical pricing, solving the problem of the uninsured, and strategies for consumer-driven health care. Over the past year she has participated in prominent debates and public forums, testified before five committees in the California legislature, appeared on popular television programs, participated in talk radio shows nationwide, and written several dozen opinion pieces on the issue of drug importation.

Ms. Pipes has held a variety of positions in both the private and public sectors. In British Columbia, the Ministry of Consumer and Corporate Affairs appointed her director and vice-chairman of the Financial Institutions Commission. She also served on the Vancouver City Planning Commission.

Ms. Pipes serves on the board of the Independent Women's Forum, the national advisory board of Capital Research Center, the board of advisors of the San Francisco Lawyers Chapter of the Federalist Society, and the State Policy Network president's advisory council. She has served as a trustee of St. Luke's Hospital Foundation in San Francisco, as a commissioner on California's Commission on Transportation Investment (CTI), and as a governor of the Donner Canadian Foundation. She was a member of California Governor Arnold Schwarzenegger's transition team in 2003.

Ms. Pipes is a member of the Mont Pelerin Society, National Association of Business Economists, and the Philadelphia Society. While in Canada she was a member of the Canadian Association for Business Economics (president for two terms) and the Association of Professional Economists of BC.

PREFACE

From leisure to labor unrest—to say nothing of politics—health care has been topic A in the United States and Canada for some time. In 1997, US movie audiences erupted into applause when actress Helen Hunt went on a verbal rampage against the restrictions in her son's fictitious managed-care plan in the hit movie, *As Good As it Gets*. Half a decade later, Hollywood sent actor Denzel Washington on a literal rampage against the dominant form of health coverage in the United States. In *John Q*, Washington takes over an emergency room in an attempt to secure his critically ill son treatment that has been denied by his health insurance company.

The Canadian health care system found itself on the silver screen in 2003 as the backdrop in the award winning film, *The Barbarian Invasions*. "I voted for medicare, I'll accept the consequences," intoned the film's main character Remy, a left-wing Canadian professor dying from cancer. Remy was responding to his son's effort to secure him better, and more comfortable care in the United States. "I'm lucky I'm not in the hall," Remy quips at another point.

Frustrations with health care have spilled off the screen and onto the streets in both countries as well. From October 2003 to March 2004, 59,000 Californians left their grocery store jobs to go on strike, causing themselves and their employers economic hardship and California shoppers inconvenience, in hopes of keeping the company-paid health insurance to which they had become accustomed.

The media portrayed the strike as emblematic of what's wrong with the US health care system—it's expensive for employers and employees alike. The leading Democratic presidential candidates, who, at the time, were engaged in a primary battle, rushed to support the workers and offer health care plans aimed at fixing the US health care system.

Three months later, labor unrest erupted 1,300 miles north in Vancouver, Canada. An estimated 43,000 health support workers struck in opposition to efforts to reduce wages and eliminate union jobs. The illegal week-long walkout forced the cancellation of more than 6,000 surgeries. Thousands of other critical diagnostic procedures such as X-Rays, CT scans, and MRIs were delayed as well.

In one case, an urgent neurological procedure had to be delayed, causing the patient's condition to deteriorate precipitously. "Once we start to cancel patients who are urgent, they can start to get sicker, sicker, and sicker," Dr. David Matheson, vice president with the Fraser Health Authority, told the *Globe and Mail*. "It increases the level of patient anxiety."[1]

I wrote this book to address the root cause of the frustration and confusion felt in the US and Canada about health care. While the strikes and movies mentioned above seem to be about distinct issues—managed care, cash-strapped hospitals, or employees having to pay a portion of their insurance premiums—in each case dysfunctional government policies and regulations have over many years created the conditions that culminated in widespread frustration, even anger, with the system.

As a former Canadian growing up under a single-payer health care system, I'm all too familiar with the limits of government-financed medicine. By the early 1990s, it became clear to me that Canada's government-run health care system was running into trouble. I realized that over the next decade, Canadians would be suffering from increased rationing, queuing for care, an absence of access to the latest technological innovations, a drug formulary system that did not give them an opportunity to acquire the latest pharmaceuticals, and few affordable private alternatives to the declining system.

In mid-1991, I was given the opportunity to run a free-market think tank in San Francisco. While this move meant leaving The

Fraser Institute and my family in Vancouver, one of the major reasons I accepted the opportunity was my frustration with the deterioration of Canada's medicare system. I wanted to live and work in a country where there was still some belief in the concept of private health care.

But in the 12 years that I have been living and working in America, I have seen a significant encroachment by government into the US system. This is an alarming trend. I address some of the key problems, including a growing number of uninsured individuals, expensive prescription drugs, and a failing managed-care system. But these pale in comparison to what is going on in Canada.

Fortunately, there are clear solutions in both countries. While I am less optimistic about the Canadian government's interest in ever allowing private alternatives, I hope this book will help to stem the tide that is flowing toward a single-payer system in the US, whereby the government would become the only financier of health care. In the last few years, flirtation with this system has been gaining increasing momentum in the US at both the state and national levels.

The goal of a health care system should be to provide all citizens with access to quality and affordable health care. These goals can only be accomplished by strengthening the sovereignty of the patient and restoring the doctor-patient relationship, both of which require reducing the role of government.

Today, people come to the United States from all over the world, including Canada, for their health care because this country is still the leader with the most recent innovations, best medical treatments, and cutting-edge pharmaceuticals. As a relatively new immigrant, I want to preserve the ability of Americans to enjoy access to the best health care system in the world. If we continue on the present path of giving more and more power to the state, this country will suffer the same problems as are being faced north of the border.

The purpose of this book is to provide the general reader with an easy-to-understand guide to the issue—an overview of the problems and clear solutions. It is written in a very accessible style, with this mainstream audience in mind. Once Americans are made aware of what a government-run, single-payer system like Canada's really means for consumers' access to health care, I believe they will realize that the growing fascination with a single-payer system is not in their best interest.

This book provides insights into the fallacies of the Canadian system, something the American media have failed to do. Government control is not the solution and if forced upon us, Americans would rebel over the lack of access to the health care that they have grown to view as a right. But it will be too late.

I hope that readers find this book engaging and useful, and I welcome comments and questions. If we are unable to stem the tide of total government control of our health, where will we go for access to the best quality care? Canadians use the US system as a safety net. America's options will be few.

Sally C. Pipes
Pacific Research Institute
July 1, 2004

FOREWORD

> "'They can't be fitted into our system of universal, free, public health services.
> 'Universal and public—yes, they could. Free, no,' Oreshchenkov confidently asserted."
> —Aleksandr I. Solzhenitsyn, *The Cancer Ward*

I regard as one of the great examples of creative imagination the few pages in Solzhenitsyn's *Cancer Ward* in which he portrays what medicine was like before the Revolution through the words of an elderly physician whose practice pre-dated 1918.[2] Solzhenitsyn himself had no personal experience on which to base his account and yet his character presents an accurate and moving vision.

The essence of that vision is the consensual relation between the patient and the physician. The patient was free to choose his physician, and the physician free to accept or reject the patient. The physician set the fee for his service and the patient paid the fee. No third party was involved in the strictly voluntary transaction between them.

That vision was a fairly accurate description of medical practice in both the United States and Canada up to the end of World War II. As Sally Pipes makes abundantly clear in this book, it no longer is.

The patient may still be free to choose a physician, though often the choice is subject to severe limits, but in most cases the patient no longer regards the physician who serves him as "his" or "her" physician responsible primarily to the patient. Similarly, the physician in most cases no longer regards himself as primarily responsible to the patient. He will be paid not by the patient, but by an insurance company or government official, who will have to approve the medical treatment the physician recommends. The insurance company or the government is effectively the physician's employer, and it is their interests, not his patients, that he is committed to serving.

Neither patients nor physicians are happy with this arrangement. So we have the paradox that while scientific medicine continues to advance, formerly incurable diseases become curable, and pain can be more readily managed, nonetheless patients and physicians express more and more dissatisfaction with medical care. What should be mutually satisfactory cooperation between patient and physician turns all too often into a bureaucratic nightmare.

In this excellent book, Sally Pipes undertakes to examine the present state of medical care in the United States and in her native Canada. She points out that although the two countries handle medical care in very different ways, both display symptoms of the same disease—excessive reliance on third-party payment. Both are headed for still more trouble unless they correctly diagnose their problems and take the right medicine.

She examines how they got into this fix and what they can and should do about it. I believe that you will find her analysis informative and lucid and her recommendations attractive.

Milton Friedman
Hoover Institution
May 19, 2004

INTRODUCTION:
Why is Health Care Such a Mess and What Can We Do About It?

> "There are a thousand hacking at the branches of evil to one who is striking at the root."
> —Henry David Thoreau

We are living longer than ever before. We are healthier than every preceding generation. Each passing year yields powerful new therapies and wonder drugs. And each passing year brings a new low in public satisfaction with health care in both the United States and Canada.

We remember the halcyon days of the family practitioner, the black bag and the home visit, the long and intensive check-ups in which doctors were literally hands-on. Why does it seem like health care costs more and delivers less? Why does health care seem today, for all its wonders, so broken?

When you bring it down to the most basic level, people ask three things from their health care providers: affordability, accessibility, and high quality.

These three factors are essential to a properly functioning health care system. And yet it is becoming harder to get these three elements in one package. You can easily find one of them, often two. It is increasingly difficult to get all three—health care that you can afford, that is always available, and is high quality.

Why is it such a mess?

To understand what is wrong with health care, it is useful to first consider the-grass-is-greener relationship between the United States and Canada.

In the United States, affordability is a critical issue, with more than 43 million Americans uninsured. Americans who do have health insurance chafe at the mounting restrictions that compromise the quality of managed care. Therefore, many US policymakers look to the advantages of Canada's single-payer system, in which coverage is universal and policies can be changed by fiat.

The single-payer system also addresses another central issue, that of access. By seeming to provide care "free," Canada's system holds great allure for US policymakers who often mistakenly conflate insurance to pay for health care with access to treatment.

In Canada, while policymakers chide their southern neighbor for subjecting patients to the vagaries of the free-market system, they secretly pine for a level of quality and access to the technological dynamism that is the hallmark of US health care. Access in Canada is also a full-blown crisis—as Canadians find themselves forced to endure long waiting lines for basic care.

This contrast is paradoxical because it appears that the systems in the United States and Canada are mirror opposites. In fact, the health care systems in both countries suffer from the same disease. Both are choking on complexity created by excessive government regulation.

The sheer complexity of regulatory intervention is causing both the United States and Canada to lose the contest to manage the third element—quality.

Constraints in costs lead to delays or outright denials of treatment, which leave consumers furious. Worst of all, the problems in the health care systems in the United States and Canada are so deep that many needed changes would be too painful to be politically feasible.

Yet something needs to be done. At a time when the rest of the service sector is ever more responsive and geared for just-in-time delivery, health care is increasingly hampered, unresponsive, and out of touch.

In the United States, the element of affordability is complicated by unrealistic public perceptions. Of course, affordability is a major public issue, with spending by government and business on health care spiraling out of control. But the complaints of US consumers often diverge from reality; the truth is that while public and business spending on health care is out of control, most Americans as individuals spend far less on health care than they imagine.

On average, Americans spend $2,350 annually on health care, just under six percent of their income. This is far less than they spend on other essentials—food, housing, and transportation. It's roughly equivalent to what they spend on such non-essentials as dining out, $2,276, and entertainment, $2,079.[3]

Sound unbelievable? Consider that, according to the Centers for Medicare and Medicaid Services (CMS), Americans reach into their own pockets for only 14 cents of every health care dollar spent.[4] Someone else paid for the other 86 percent. Why, then, is perception so contrary to reality?

The reason is the US tax code, which for decades has subsidized the sponsorship of health insurance by our employers. This isn't the case with other necessities that are of similar importance in people's lives—housing, food, and transportation. We are not outraged that we must bear the full cost of our grocery bill, nor do we expect our employers to pay for the car we need to get us to work.

Free health care?

Most Americans are, however, so unused to directly bearing the full cost of health care that they've grown accustomed to thinking of it as an entitlement. It is for this reason that politicians have grown used to speaking of health care as if it were a constitutional right.

Using employers and the tax code to subsidize the cost of health care does more than give American consumers an unrealistic idea about the true cost of health care. It also gives every working American a stake in the current system, making the prospect of reform doubly difficult.

In Canada, health care is not just perceived as a right—it is one. Every Canadian can, in theory, count on free, comprehensive health care promised by the Canada Health Act. The only alternative to this health care system is to seek care in the United States. Actually to compete with the national system in Canada is, with a few exceptions, a crime. Obviously, to change a system as embedded and universal as Canada's is a daunting task.

Change in a system is possible, however, whenever the system finally hits its limits and starts to produce noxious results. The need for change in both countries is apparent. In the United States, this need is expressed in the widespread rebellion by the insured against rationing enforced by managed care. Americans are rebelling over bureaucratic interference in the doctor-patient relationship.

Further, many are worried about the fate of the more than 43.6 million Americans who have no health insurance coverage at all. Few understand the extent to which these problems, especially the legions of the uninsured, are the unintended consequences of the US approach of employer-sponsored health insurance.

Because health insurance is linked with employment, coverage moves up and down with the business cycle. Everyone is pleased when the number of people covered by job-based insurance increases during economic booms. But when these levels decline during periods of recession, people lose their jobs and insurance—and this usually happens just as government safety-net programs are strapped for funding.

This cycle, already painful, will only become more acute as premiums rise. The Kaiser Family Foundation reports that health care premiums for families in employer-sponsored plans soared 13.9 percent in 2003, the third year of double-digit growth.[5]

In Canada, the system is also hitting its limits. Provincial governments have been utterly unable to control costs. The response in Canada has been to shift the costs from the strapped Canadian taxpayer to the Canadian patient, who pays the price in the non-monetary forms of increased pain and suffering, lost wages, and the expense of traveling to the United States for prompt treatment.

Thirty years of government intervention has left Canadian health care suffering from long waiting times for critical procedures, lack of access to current technology, and a brain drain of doctors. Thousands of patients languish in wait for Magnetic Resonance Imaging (MRI) machines, though they can easily get a scan for a family pet for $20. Canadian political leaders who extol the virtues of their system can often be found in US hospitals the instant they cannot get in to see a Canadian doctor.[6]

It is time to acknowledge a basic truth: In both countries, these problems originate from ill-conceived government intervention in the marketplace.

What can we do about it?

In the United States, the public needs to know that it can safely move away from a tax system that encourages employer-provided health insurance. In Canada, the public must be weaned off a system in which public health care brooks no competition. In both instances, less government intervention can yield greater affordability, access, and quality.

Of course, if reformers simply rail at government intervention, they will only be tilting at windmills. Reformers have a responsibility to see the world as it is. It is our intent here to suggest practical and achievable changes, while supporting the three basic human health care needs. Any plan that fails in one of the key values—affordability, access, and quality—will fail the test of public acceptance, and deservedly so.

Reform in the United States must close the gap for the uninsured, so that all Americans are protected against catastrophic loss from unexpected health care needs. For the insured, reform must address quality and the deterioration of the doctor-patient relationship. In Canada, health care reform must reverse the growing crisis of rationing, achieved by creating long waiting lists for care. It must also reverse the deteriorating state of Canadian medical and pharmaceutical technology.

In both instances, incremental and relatively painless reform can be achieved by moving toward greater personal control of health care. We need more freedom to allow the health care market to flourish.

In the United States, reformers must:

- Eliminate the preferential tax treatment was given to employers as a concession at the end of World War II when wage and price controls were in effect.
- Give individuals the opportunity to purchase health care with pre-tax dollars regardless of whether they have a job or not. Such a legislative change would break down the third-party payment system and reform the way health care costs are paid. Health insurance would be returned to its proper role of providing coverage for catastrophic events. Individuals could join all manner of voluntary groups, seeking the best deal and the health care plan that is right for them.
- Move from managed care—the dominant system of insurance in the United States—to a system of consumer-directed plans such as HSAs, defined contribution plans in which individuals are empowered to make the most important decisions affecting their health.

Part One

The US Solution:
Expand Consumer Choice

- Abolish state regulations and mandates that needlessly complicate health care policy and make health care more expensive. By opening up the market, insurance companies should be able to offer, and consumers to purchase, insurance on a nationwide basis.
- Reform medical malpractice insurance and a system that currently encourages lawsuit abuse.
- Remove the barriers to entry that make the health care industry a restricted monopoly.
- Restructure Medicare so that it becomes a menu of choices among privately run, competitive insurance programs similar to those enjoyed by federal employees.

In Canada, reformers must:

- Make provincial insurance plans—and the taxes that fund them—voluntary.
- Open government plans to direct competition from private insurers, both non-profit and for-profit.
- Allow doctors to charge whatever they like, and to organize their practices in any way they choose.
- Permit private companies to build and operate the necessary capital-intensive facilities that Canada currently lacks—and to do so at a profit.

In this book, Part One details the problems with US health care, how those problems developed over time, and offers solutions. Part Two takes a similar look at the Canadian health care system.

CHAPTER ONE:
What is the Real Nature of Health Care in the United States?

The myth of the US health care system is that it is a freewheeling, cold-hearted, for-profit system. And it is true that for-profit insurance companies, medical supply corporations, hospitals, and physician practices are notable actors in the US health care environment. It is for this reason that the United States has the most dispersed and dynamic health care system in the world.

Dr. Michael Porter, noted professor at the Harvard Business School, writes, "Competition should force providers to equal or exceed the value created by the best in their region or even nationally. For the most part, however, health care competition is local. Such competition insulates mediocre providers from market pressures and inhibits the spread of best practices and innovations."[7]

However, few realize how US tax policy distorts the market for health care and health insurance. Federal and state governments, too, are hardly passive observers on the sidelines. Government has been the largest single player in the US health care marketplace since the 1960s.

In 1960, *direct* federal spending accounted for nine percent of health spending. By 2001, direct federal spending was up to 32 percent of all health care spending. Add in local and state efforts, and government *directly* pays for *45 percent* of health care spending in America.[8]

Such direct spending does not include the value of tax subsidies, the imposed costs of regulations on private insurers, or the tax-payer funds that are used to provide health insurance to federal government workers under the Federal Employees Health Benefits Program (FEHBP). When you consider these costs, the reality becomes apparent—despite the strong role of free enterprise, US health care is more socialist than not.

US hospitals spend billions of dollars a year just filling out government forms. Some hospitals in California answer to as many as 39 governmental bodies and must file as many as 65 periodic reports.

In recent years, the federal government has begun directly regulating health insurance.

Noted economists John Goodman and Gerald Musgrave report that these "regulatory requirements intrude in a highly visible way on the activities of medical staff and affect virtually every aspect of medical practice."[9]

Government is now the largest financier of health coverage in the United States, spending $587 billion in 2000.[10]

Medicare alone purchases one-third of all hospital care and pays for nearly 20 percent of physician fees.[11]

The government also operates the Veterans Administration (VA) health system, the country's single largest health care provision system, spending roughly $20 billion a year to serve four million veterans in 1,300 facilities.[12]

Add to these explicit costs the intrusion of regulations that direct almost all health care activity. The American Health Lawyers Association's comprehensive publication on health care law, *United States Health Care Laws and Rules 2004-2005*, is so heavy that customers must make special shipping arrangements if they order more than five copies. And this just accounts for the federal load.[13] Regulating health care is a favored activity of state governments, which fill state statute books with provisions that health insurance must cover.

There are over 1,500 state-mandated benefits in effect across the United States, most of them enacted since 1990, covering benefits, specifying which providers are included, and identifying people who should be covered.
(Source: "State Legislative Health Care and Insurance Issues: 2001 Survey of Plans," Blue Cross Blue Shield Association.)

After passing the Health Maintenance Organization (HMO) Act of 1973 and the Consolidated Omnibus Budget Reconciliation Act (COBRA) of 1985, Congress has accelerated its involvement through the Health Insurance Portability and Accountability Act (HIPAA) of 1996 and the Mental Health Parity Act of 1996.

Washington also issued federal mandates to insurers for minimum maternity stays in 1996 and breast reconstruction surgery in 1998. Other regulations that are currently before Congress include a Patients' Bill of Rights and full mental health parity.

Seemingly neutral factors as tax law also distort health care economics, by rewarding some forms of health care (employer-provided) and punishing others (self-insured).

In the name of controlling costs, the federal government has become heavily involved in persecuting doctors over allegations of fraud and abuse. "The insanity is running wild," says Dr. Michael Harris of Traverse City, Michigan. "A friend and son of one of my patients was arrested, handcuffed, and put in jail today for 'insurance fraud,' for billing for the midwife's services at a birthing center. He is one of the most honest physicians I know."
(Source: Michael Harris, "Are You Next?," Letter to Editor, AAPS News, volume 57, no. 12 (December 2001). Available at http://www.aapsonline.org/newsletters/dec01.htm.)

CHAPTER TWO:
How Did Big Government become Big Medicine?

One reason why government intervention has grown to such an extent is because of a decidedly ambiguous attitude toward regulation on the part of physicians.

This may seem counterintuitive. After all, the American Medical Association (AMA) emerged as a powerful force in the twentieth century by defeating plans for nationalized health insurance. However, the AMA and state medical organizations have less publicly advocated another goal—to protect the physician's place at the center of health care arrangements.[14]

It is easy to understand why so many good physicians would be hostile to third-party payers. Many doctors do not want to be given a choice between being employees of large, for-profit organizations, or being forced into large group practices to attract business. "The dislike of physicians for 'socialized medicine' is well known," writes historian Paul Starr. "But their distaste for corporate capitalism in medical practice was equally strong."[15]

Thus, physicians organized to pass restrictive laws that prevented the "corporate practice of medicine," such as prepaid lodge, union, and tenement doctors, many of these early forms of managed care. They also sought government licensure of both physicians and medical schools, restricting the supply of caregivers and turning what was a once low-paying profession into a profession of high status and high income. In many ways, physicians have

often acquiesced or even abetted the growth of government intervention in health care.

An even greater source of government intervention in health care
is the ambition of social planners. The history of health care in
recent decades is largely the history of social planners intervening
to undo the unintended consequences of their earlier interven-
tions. When it comes to health care policy, social planners have
never taken to heart the Hippocratic Oath, "First, do no harm."

Too many or not enough?

Consider the history of public policy and hospitals. In 1946, President Harry Truman signed the Hospital Survey and Construction
Act, known as the Hill-Burton Act, which has since pumped $4.6
billion of federal taxpayer money into the building of non-profit
hospitals. In exchange for a federal subsidy, these hospitals were
obliged to provide charity care for the destitute (an early attempt
to provide a national safety net).[16]

All of this, of course, cost money; so later government planners
decided that America had the opposite problem—too many hospitals and too much high-tech equipment. So Congress passed a law
giving planners more power over the approval of new hospitals
and expansions of current hospitals. In 1974, the federal government cracked down on costs even more with a Certification of
Need (CON) mandate as part of the National Health Planning and
Resources Development Act. These measures have been utter fail-
ures at cost control.[17]

The federal government's right foot on the gas, left foot on the
brake approach to health planning wasn't limited to hospitals. In
the 1950s and 1960s, government planners projected a physician
shortage and proceeded to pump billions of dollars into medical
schools. By the 1980s, planners perceived that the problem was
that the United States had too many doctors.[18]

President Clinton's 1993 health care plan sought to increase the
number of general practitioners relative to specialists (a fine-tun-

ing that managed care is already able to achieve in the market-place). In the Balanced Budget Act of 1997, Congress devoted taxpayer money to pay hospitals to reduce the number of physicians they train.[19]

Incredibly, while the government restricts the numbers of specialists, it is still subsidizing specialist training to the tune of $6 billion a year. "It is somewhat numbing to think that we need a government program to correct the 'problem' of specialist over-supply that itself is the result of another government program," writes health economist David Dranove. "In such ways, one regulatory program begets another."[20]

State edicts

State legislators, too, have been eager to impose their vision on health care. Upset with variation in the market among health insurance policies, states have mandated that each policy must cover a host of procedures.

The unintended consequence of such mandates is to increase the cost of insurance. How does government react? The very same politicians who fomented this crisis create new government programs to regulate health care even more or expand mandated coverage.

Consider the Health Maintenance Act of 1973, which mandated that employers of more than 25 people must offer their employees at least one health maintenance organization (HMO) option.[21] Measures like these, well intentioned as many of them are, have driven up costs and forced many middle-aged workers into unemployment, with a corresponding lack of health care coverage.

Thus the logic of intervention continues, one solution begetting one crisis after another—until breakdown, forcing the entire system to become government run.

CHAPTER THREE:
How is Washington Responding to Health Care Now?

"Politics is the art of looking for trouble, finding it everywhere, diagnosing it incorrectly, and applying the wrong remedies."
—Groucho Marx

Washington policymakers are bipolar when it comes to health policy.

Consider the issue of prescription drugs. One the one hand, policymakers applaud prescription drugs, as they should. After all, properly used pharmaceuticals save health care purchasers money and improve the lives of patients. And policymakers view pharmaceuticals as so important that they are willing to spend billions of taxpayer dollars to include them in the government-run Medicare program.

Washington's other personality views the issue a bit differently. While never disputing the importance or value of the product, it attacks the industry that produces it as greedy. It seeks to pass laws and regulations that would make it legal to import pharmaceuticals from Canada and directly regulate the purchase price of drugs, which would cripple the industry and prevent it from producing the next generation of life-enhancing drugs.

Washington is also often at odds with itself over what the central problem with health care is. When economic times are good, as they were in the late 1990s, policymakers become critically concerned with ensuring quality by passing regulations.

The Patients' Bill of Rights (PBR), which actually passed both houses of Congress in 2001 but was never signed into law, is an example of this concern. This bill, which may be reintroduced at some point, provides an excellent example of policymakers' urge to regulate and control health care, replacing the informal evolution of the market with dictates of central planners. If ultimately successful, the PBR will mark another round of expansion of the federal government into private health care.

Like most other government efforts in health care, this bill works against its purported goals. The House bill, for example, declares, "Congress finds that continually increasing the complex Government regulation of the health care delivery system has proven ineffective in restraining costs and is itself counterproductive in fulfilling its purposes and detrimental to the care of patients."[22]

That declaration is attended, however, by 237 pages worth of new regulations.

Such regulation doesn't come cheap. If passed into law, the bill's costs will be passed on to those who purchase private insurance. The Congressional Budget Office estimates that the PBR alone would increase premiums by 4.1 percent over what they otherwise would be. The result will be another 1.2 million Americans who would find their employers no longer able to afford to offer them medical insurance.[23]

In times of economic downturn, Washington's focus shifts to the issue of the uninsured. That's the current case and the reason why the PBR is on the back burner.

Part of Washington's bi-polar condition stems from the views of the two political parties. Democrats, in general, favor government regulation while Republicans, with many, many exceptions, espouse a more free-market orientation.

The 2004 presidential race bears this out. Democratic presidential nominee John Kerry offers a $1 trillion plan that puts the taxpayer on the hook for paying the preponderance of medical claims of more than $50,000. In return, he would demand that employers offer health insurance to all of their workers, regardless of employment tenure or number of hours worked.

The health care agenda pursued by the Bush administration and some Congressional leaders is centered on increasing the role of private markets and market mechanisms in health care. The idea is that by reducing regulations and, therefore, reducing the price of insurance, more Americans will be able to afford it.

An excellent example of this agenda in action is the Health Savings Accounts, HSAs, which passed as part of the Medicare Prescription Drug Improvement and Modernization Act of 2003, signed by President Bush on December 8, 2003. This legislation promises to extend prescription drug benefits to Medicare recipients in 2006. HSAs are totally tax-free savings accounts in which individuals can accumulate money to pay out-of-pocket medical expenses not covered by health insurance plans.

Unlike health insurance, money contributed to HSAs is not "use it or lose it" by nature. Any money not used in one year can be kept in the account, earning interest or market returns, for use in the future. HSAs, when combined with high-deductible insurance policies, promise to be an excellent choice for many Americans.

In addition to tax-free HSAs, President Bush proposed in his 2004 State of the Union address that the actual premium of catastrophic insurance policies should be tax deductible, provided that it accompanies an HSA. The president also called for refundable tax credits of $1,000 per individual and $3,000 per family to help low income Americans purchase health insurance.

In addition, the president has endorsed Association Health Plans, an arrangement that would allow small businesses to band together to obtain access to more favorable insurance rates.

CHAPTER FOUR:
What is a Third-party Payer— and What's So Bad About It?

"If you think health care is expensive now, wait until you see what it costs when it's free."
—P.J. O'Rourke

"I doubt that a single doctor I have seen over the last 10 years would know me if he or she fell over me in the street, including my current 'primary-care physician' whom I've probably seen six or seven times over the past two years," a woman wrote to the *New York Times* medical columnist, Jennifer Steinhauer. "I don't get the feeling the doctors care one whit about me as an individual."[24]

At one time, private health insurance in the United States was primarily a fee-for-service model. Americans chose their doctors, and trusted them to determine the best course of care. For those who were privately insured, the patient's health insurance company paid the majority of the cost. The doctor-patient relationship constituted the core of this US health care system, a system that was deemed by many as among the best in the world.

However, for third-party payers the system was less than ideal, both for politicians watching health care costs gobble up Medicare/Medicaid budgets, and for employers watching health insurance costs. By the end of the 1970s, General Motors was complaining that it sent larger annual checks to its health care providers than it did to US Steel, its largest supplier.[25]

Both government and companies responded by placing limits on providers—and directly interfering in the practice of medicine. In Medicare, this meant clamping down on price controls and failing to update benefit packages. Medicare recipients, for example, have just recently secured limited coverage for prescription drugs, even though drugs are a critical component in the health care system.

In the private sector, managed care emerged to systematically organize patient care and control costs. The result in both cases was the deterioration of the doctor-patient relationship. Payers, after all, insisted on a say. And, since he who pays the piper calls the tune, they got it.

The result was that many of the 177 million Americans with private, employer-sponsored insurance found themselves pushed into managed care.[26] Employers—the payers—chose to limit their employees' options in exchange for lower costs. As a rule, people are generally happy with their choices, even difficult ones, as long as those choices are truly theirs. But all of a sudden, Americans were told they could no longer see their doctor because he wasn't on a managed care list, or they couldn't go straight to a specialist as they had in years past, but first had to see a primary-care doctor.

By 2000, 163 million Americans—92 percent of those with employer-sponsored health insurance—were enrolled in some form of managed care.[27] Dissatisfaction escalated and a wave of complaints followed.

There is no systematic evidence that managed care has reduced the overall quality of US health care.[28] It is clear, however, that managed care limits patients' choices and, at some level, rations care. And in a country as large as the United States, this inevitably produces more than a handful of horror stories.

Middle America's anxiety about health care once centered on whether people would lose insurance in an economic downturn. In the 1990s, with health maintenance organization horror stories gaining attention, Americans started shifting their primary worry from being uninsured, to the fear that their insurance would fail to provide them with coverage they might need. When asked

In March 2001, Dr. Donald Palmisano, a trustee of the American Medical Association, told a congressional committee of a case in which a man died of stomach cancer after failing for two and a half years to get his insurance company to pay for the treatment the company's own physician recommended. (Source: Donald J. Palmisano, "Statement of the American Medical Association to the Committee on Energy and Commerce Subcommittee on Health," United States House of Representatives, March 15, 2001.)

about HMOs in a national poll conducted in 2001, slightly more than half had an unfavorable opinion of them.[29]

The problem remains that the largest customers in the US health care market are not the ultimate consumers, the people who must bear the marginal costs. The largest customers are third-party payers—employers and insurance companies. Added to these ranks are the federal and state governments that provide health care for 71 million Americans, including some "double-dippers" who receive both employer plans and government programs.

Having third parties make so many purchasing decisions reduces the ability of consumers to call the shots. In a normal market, unhappiness with third-party agents would prompt many consumers to find other competitive providers. Not so in health care. The strong gravitational pull of the tax code influences the purchase of health insurance by employers. (After all, if you could cut your grocery bill in half by funneling the purchase through an employer, you might rely on them to buy your food as well.)

Employers, on the other hand, understand that health insurance is a part of their employees' total compensation package. It's good business to purchase health insurance for employees because it's a pre-tax purchase and group coverage can often be bought at a lower price than an individual policy. Employees have come to expect it as a part of the job, and some employers use health coverage to entice new workers to their firm. But the disadvantages of this system are beginning to outweigh the advantages.

Americans expect salary increases as well as medical insurance, yet a dollar spent on insurance premium increases is a dollar that cannot go toward a raise. The two are in direct competition, especially in recession years like 2001. The incentives of third-party payment, which give patients little reason to choose services or providers on the basis of cost, will continue to drive such increases.

CHAPTER FIVE:
Is Managed Care Good or Bad?

As is often the case, popular culture delivered the verdict on Health Maintenance Organizations, the most restrictive, and for a time promising, form of what is known as managed care. "F*** HMOs. Bastard pieces of s***," exclaimed actress Helen Hunt portraying a single mother in the 1997 movie *As Good as It Gets*. A nonplussed doctor replies to the apologetic Hunt, "It's okay. Actually, I think that's their technical name." Theater audiences erupted into applause.

In 2002, Denzel Washington starred in a movie whose entire script was written to attack the penny-pinching practices of HMOs. In the movie *John Q*, a working man, played by Washington, holds an emergency room hostage in order to get a heart transplant for his seriously ill son. Like the rationing by queue in Canada, managed care has produced its share of horror stories.

Ian Malone, a Washington State infant born with brain damage, was initially denied coverage for his care by his family's HMO, which suggested that his parents should give Ian up for adoption in order to get coverage.[30] These stories, trumpeted in newspapers and on television newsmagazine shows, have been a cause of anxiety for Americans.

Nothing new

Forms of managed care have a history as long as formal medicine in the United States—and they've been under attack by some organized interest the entire time. "America's romance with the health maintenance organization reflects all the contradictions inherent in the US health care system," write the editors of *Health Affairs*, the preeminent journal of health policy. "They want to eliminate waste, yet they bristle at mandatory preauthorization of care. They have high-quality, proven health care treatment, yet they reject practice guidelines issued by insurers."[31]

Managed care first emerged in the early twentieth century as industrialization and urbanization presented new challenges to be solved by entrepreneurial organizations. Industrialization meant large numbers of individuals were often working in accident-prone environments and employers responded by hiring doctors to keep employees healthy. "In 1930," notes Pulitzer Prize-winning historian Paul Starr, "these programs covered an estimated 540,000 workers in mining and lumbering and approximately 530,000 railway employees."[32]

In densely populated cities, fraternal societies and lodges were paying hard-pressed doctors, who were in ample supply since governments had not yet restricted medical education, as little as $2.00 per member annually to take care of people who got sick.[33]

This is a classic story of bottom-up capitalism. Families were willing to pay a modest, predictable sum of money to ensure that should a member need care in the future, they wouldn't face crushing bills. Many physicians, who were hungry for patients, were more than willing to strike such bargains. More established doctors, however, feared the competition and called on governments to do something about it. The result was a steady march of increasing income.

HMOs, from their earliest form to their remnants today, exist to address two issues central to health care. First, they offer insurance, and offered informal insurance long before the formal industry existed. HMOs also serve to coordinate and deliver cost effective care. In its early forms, this often meant housing doctors on large industrial work projects. More recently, it meant dealing with a major flaw in the US health care environment: the third-party-payer system that renders both patients and doctors completely insensitive to the cost of health care services.

Government loves me; it loves me not

Governments in the United States also have a love-hate relationship with HMOs. State governments, at the behest of organized medicine, outlawed early forms of HMOs. Yet a few decades later, national policymakers became infatuated with them. Facing the threat of nationalized health insurance, the federal government subsidized, and all but mandated, what the states for so long had used the law to prevent.

The Health Maintenance Act of 1973 established government subsidies for the creation of non-profit HMOs, with the integrated Kaiser, which wasn't subsidized, as the model. It also mandated that employers of more than 25 employees offer employees at least one HMO option.[34]

In its modern form, managed care emerged to control costs by placing limits on both health care providers and consumers, at the behest of the buyers. On the supply side, managed-care companies attempt to keep costs in line by rationalizing care, which in practice means negotiating lower fees with physicians and hospitals, shifting risks to doctors, and managing provider networks that limit consumer choice of providers and hospitals.

On the demand side, managed care clamps down on patients in more subtle ways. Even while companies work to reduce the out-of-pocket expense for individuals, they seek to raise the non-monetary costs of using expensive care. They do this primarily by requiring patients to see a primary care doctor first, who will then coordinate all specialty care.

As the cost of health insurance became an important issue in the 1980s and 1990s, employers and policymakers again turned to the HMOs for help. At the start of the 1980s, there were fewer than 100 HMOs in existence. Five years later, more than 500 HMOs were open for business.[35] In 2001, there were 531 HMOs.[36] By

2000, 163 million Americans—92 percent of those with employer-sponsored health insurance—were enrolled in some form of managed care.[37]

Managed care has delivered mixed results. It has certainly kept costs lower than what they otherwise would have been. From 1994 to 1997, average health benefit costs remained roughly constant, a remarkable achievement.[38] Health care economist David Dranove estimates that managed care reduced health care spending in 2000 alone by $300 billion compared to what was estimated in 1993 by the Congressional Budget Office.[39] That's a savings of nearly $2,000 per privately insured American.

There is little evidence that it has done so, in the aggregate, at the expense of quality. "Each month's new studies generally confirm what many have already concluded," writes Dranove. "Namely, that the quality of care in [managed care organizations] is comparable to that under traditional indemnity insurance."[40]

However, polls show that managed care has taken a toll on physicians, who, over the decade of its emergence, showed declines in professional satisfaction. "Physicians showed the most dissatisfaction with their professional autonomy, amount of leisure time available, and with the time available to spend with patients," reports a *Reuters Health* wire story.[41] And as the $300 billion a year reduction in health spending would indicate, they're frustrated with having to accept lower incomes. "In 1986 about 75 percent of the physicians said that they were satisfied or very satisfied with their total earnings," Dr. Dana Gelb Safran told *Reuters Health*. "In 1997, that number dropped to 55 percent." [42]

Under attack

The 1990s rush to HMOs spurred a predictable backlash, once again. As a booming economy shifted the central health care concern from the uninsured to the quality of care for those who had insurance, an unholy coalition of doctors, patient advocates, and trial lawyers attacked the industry on multiple fronts. HMOs found themselves on the defensive in court and in statehouses.

On the national level, Congress debated the Patients' Bill of Rights, which, if it were to become law, would eviscerate the HMO business model. Most important, the market moved away from HMOs. Employers, the largest purchaser of health insurance, shifted away from HMOs, just as they shifted from traditional indemnity insurance a decade earlier.

In 2003, only 24 percent of people covered by employer-purchased insurance were in HMOs. The less restrictive Preferred Provider Organization (PPO) had emerged as the insurance organizational form of choice, increasing from 11 percent of covered individuals in 1988 to 54 percent in 2003.[43]

"Today the conventional contents of the managed care 'toolbox'—most notably, aggressive utilization management, selective contracting with caregivers, and financial incentives to physicians to limit care—play much less prominent roles in health insurance business strategy than they did in the mid-1990s," write professors M. Gregg Bloche and David M. Studdert. "Americans with health insurance have more freedom to choose among doctors and hospitals and to obtain costly tests and treatments."[44]

CHAPTER SIX:
Why Can't We Get the Best Health Care at the Best Prices?

The problems created by government intervention, coupled with the distorting effects of the tax code on health care, are two great sources for individuals and doctors in the private market. "This fundamentally irrational system is designed for conflict and turmoil, for political posturing and lawsuits," writes Lawrence Mirel, the District of Columbia's commissioner for insurance and securities. "It's definitely not designed for providing the best health care at the best prices."[45]

The very nature of prepaid medicine prompts people to overuse health care services. The federal tax subsidy makes health care inexpensive compared to other goods and services, and that alone would cause Americans to demand more of it even without the third-party payment system. Throw in the third-party payer factor—and require that medicine must be purchased in advance each year—and demand goes through the roof.

What do we mean by a system of prepaid medicine? To fully understand the negative effects of the current prepaid system, it is necessary to also appreciate that the term "medical insurance" is a bit of misnomer.

"The general definition of an 'insurable event'—from traffic accidents to tornadoes—is something that is first, unlikely to happen; second, will come without warning; and, third, is not something that the person who is insured wants to happen," notes Mirel.

"That definition applies to such catastrophic health events as serious illness or injury. But it does not apply to routine health maintenance."[46]

Homeowners' insurance covers fires, trees collapsing on roofs, and other similarly large events. Automobile insurance covers major dents, broken glass, and total wrecks. But what travels under the name of health insurance in the United States has expanded to cover just about everything, including the routine, the predictable, and the easily affordable. It's as if automobile insurance paid for the 3,000-mile oil change and the 30,000-mile tune up, or if homeowners' insurance paid to replace burnt out light bulbs and repair leaky faucets.

Milton Friedman cautions that there is no such thing as a free lunch. By lowering the price, insurance increases the amount of services and products purchased. This, in turn, creates new distortions, as the largest portion of the cost is paid in a lump sum premium regardless of how many services someone uses.

Visits may or may not require a token co-payment, set at a flat fee, or, under traditional indemnity insurance, a percentage of the total costs. Patients are thus extremely desensitized to the cost of any service they receive. "People think a doctor's office visit costs less than a haircut, which is frightening," says Ryan Levin of Destiny Health in Oak Brook, Illinois. "Because they think it's so cheap, they're less concerned about whether to utilize care or not."[47]

This system drives up costs. The increase in costs, in turn, forces managed-care companies to issue edicts that compromise the doctor-patient relationship. Rising costs also push more people into managed care, while ultimately increasing the numbers of Americans who are uninsured.

Such overuse drives double-digit cost increases. In response, insurance companies can only:

- pass on the costs in the form of premium increases,
- attempt to reduce the fees they pay providers,
- or work to limit the services they offer enrollees.

The first option, raising premiums, exacerbates the problem of the uninsured, as both businesses and individuals obey the law of supply and demand—resulting in less insurance purchased as prices increase.

Health care actuary Mark Litow estimates that each one percent increase in health insurance premiums, over and above normal trends, increases the uninsured rate by 0.3 percent.[48]

Annual out-of-pocket health care only costs the uninsured $241, according to a recent study by Yale economist Bradley Herring. Two-thirds of the cost of care consumed by the uninsured is essentially donated.[49] Many people simply won't buy health insurance if it's too expensive. So when premiums are raised, we see a rise in the level of the uninsured.

The second option, controlling costs by reducing fees, is like squeezing a balloon—the costs will only "pop out" somewhere else, in the form of reduced care or limited choices.

The third option, controlling costs by limiting care, forces patients to first see a primary-care doctor, who then coordinates all specialty care. This is meant to actively discourage people from coming to the doctor's office; in effect, it is a form of rationing. Like Canada's single-payer system, it pushes some costs onto other parties. Physicians, for example, bear the burden of increased bureaucracy and paperwork. Patients are forced to spend time asking permission of "gatekeepers" before they can turn to specialists.

The American public, at least for now, has rejected the most restrictive forms.

CHAPTER SEVEN:
What's Wrong with Tying
Health Care to Jobs?

"We have become so accustomed to employer-provided medical care that we regard it as part of the natural order," said economist and Noble laureate Milton Friedman. "Yet it is thoroughly illogical."[50]

It is important to remember that private health insurance is not the same as a free market in health insurance or health care. In a free market, buyers and sellers, including corporations, unions, and mutual benefit societies, would be at liberty to strike bargains for any number of health care arrangements. This is not the case in the United States today.

Sixty-three percent of Americans are covered by private, employer-based insurance. When individuals who are enrolled in government health insurance programs are excluded from the pool, this number jumps to 74 percent.[51]

However, despite the rising dissatisfaction with managed care, it is important to remember that most people are relatively content with their private insurance. For four years running, two-thirds of respondents to a Harris Poll have given their current plan an A or B grade, and would recommend it to a friend or family member.[52] Indeed, it is the satisfaction with private arrangements that has repeatedly frustrated efforts for universal health insurance.

Remember the "Harry and Louise" television spots that won the debate against the Clintons' attempt to create national health care in 1993? They informed people that the Clinton plan might force them to give up their private arrangements.

Still, despite a relatively high level of satisfaction, the fact remains that the current structure of the private health care marketplace produces a distorted outcome that is fueling growing consumer anger among some of the insured, while swelling the ranks of the uninsured.

As illogical as it seems to academics, the linkage between employment and health care makes some sense to average working people. It provides extensive coverage, since most Americans live in a household where at least one person is working. Employers tend to hire healthy people. When there are large pools of healthy people, the risks associated with those who are major users of the health care system, are spread out.

But there is a downside to using the tax code to push health insurance. First, there are issues of fundamental fairness. By making medical insurance cheaper for individuals employed by third parties, it becomes more expensive for the unemployed and students, who must use after-tax dollars to purchase care.

The health care paradox

Assuming a marginal tax rate of 40 percent, a person without employer-provided health insurance must earn *$1.67 to buy $1 of health insurance.*[53]

Employers spent, on average, $3,713 per employee enrolled in HMOs in 2000 and an additional $300 for those who chose less restrictive Preferred Provider Organizations (PPOs).[54] But an individual would have to earn more than $6,000 to purchase the same health care plan.

Looking at it from the opposite direction, people can cut their personal cost of health insurance by almost one-half by having their employers purchase it for them. The federal tax subsidy for employer-based health insurance is worth $110 billion a year—perhaps the largest single distortion in the US health care system.[55]

Artificially lower costs lead to the fundamental problem with US health insurance. "(Medical insurance) contains a built-in contradiction," writes Lawrence Mirel. "The insurance system works best when the fewest people use it (i.e., make claims); the health-care system works best when the most people use it (i.e., get check-ups and tests and vaccinations). The goals are incompatible."[56]

This contradiction produces a paradox—the reason health care is so expensive in the United States is because it's so cheap. "The irony," note economists John Goodman and Gerald Musgrave in their book, *Patient Power: Solving America's Health Care Crisis*, "is that health care costs are rising because, for individual patients, medical care is cheap, not expensive."[57]

Thus, the economics of an employment-based health insurance system fuel the crisis of the uninsured. Since 1987, there have never been fewer than 31 million uninsured Americans.[58] Studies of the uninsured have found that roughly four out of five have jobs (usually very low paying employment), or are part of a family where there is at least one working member.[59] Two out of three belong to families with incomes less than $50,000.[60]

Health insurance is a take-it-or-leave-it proposition—and some decide to leave it. An employer typically offers a plan of its choosing and often requires that employees must pay a set amount out of their income toward the premium. The employee's share of the premium can be significant and is likely to increase from year to year. Low-income workers, particularly if they are young and healthy, may feel they are better off keeping this money as income and forgoing the insurance coverage.

An even bigger problem is coverage for family members. Many employers require employees to pay the full cost of coverage for dependents from their salaries. In 2002, the average annual worker contribution for employee-only coverage was $454, but it was $2,084 for family coverage.[61]

Double dipping

Dual-income families present a special dilemma.

A family where both spouses work can obtain coverage from two insurance policies without paying out-of-pocket toward the cost—a great deal for the family. But having two sources of insurance coverage is extremely inefficient. One hundred percent coverage of medical events leads to over-consumption of health care, which results in higher premiums in future years. As a result, these costs are passed on in the form of higher premiums for one-earner families, and ultimately higher costs for everyone.

Health-insurance coverage is also concentrated among workers in large firms. Ninety-nine percent of firms with 200 or more workers offered health insurance in 2002, against only 61 percent of firms with fewer than 200 workers.[62]

There are two main reasons for this disparity. First, large employers have enough workers that they can self-insure their benefits. This allows them to escape state regulations and mandates and instead be subject to the less bureaucratic federal Employee Retirement Income Security Act (ERISA). While self-insuring shifts the risk to the employer, it also enables companies to offer coverage at a lower cost.

Second, states often heap additional regulations on to the small group market, usually defined as businesses with 50 or fewer workers. As a result, small group policies in many states have higher premiums per person than individual policies.

Other factors may lead small businesses to forgo health insurance. Small companies are more likely to employ low-wage workers for which health insurance premiums represent a larger percentage of compensation. When insurance premiums rise at a faster rate than wages, this disproportionately affects the compensation of low-wage workers.

Small businesses that can't afford to see employee compensation rise by large amounts will tend to react by dropping insurance coverage. Also, minimum-wage workers are shut out from receiving health insurance on the job because the law specifies that they must receive their compensation as wages.

Due to the nature of employer-sponsored health insurance, the tax subsidy for the wealthiest workers (those with annual incomes greater than $100,000) averages $2,780 per worker, while the subsidy for low-income workers ranges from zero to only a few hundred dollars per worker.[63] Americans with incomes greater than $100,000 account for 14 percent of the population yet garner more than a quarter of the total tax subsidy. In contrast, the nearly six in 10 families with incomes of less than $50,000 a year enjoy just under 29 percent of the total value of the tax subsidy.[64] This disparity contributes to the large number of low-income workers who do not have any health insurance—hardly the outcome expected from "liberal" social policy.

Remarkably, many of the same people who proclaim the plight of the uninsured as a national shame will turn around and ardently defend adding new mandates to employment-based health insurance. They should realize that adding new mandates expands the ranks of the unemployed and uninsured. They should also realize that the employer-sponsored model made more sense when households typically had one breadwinner who tended to remain with one company over his or her entire career. It makes much less sense today, in a world where individuals change jobs often and families are composed of two earners, each of whom may take time out of the workplace at some time over a working career.

CHAPTER EIGHT:
Is There a Better Way Than Employer-sponsored Health Care?

Employer-sponsored health care may soon undergo the same sort of changes that have come to retirement savings. For much of the twentieth century, workers relied on administratively complex, defined-benefit pensions—those that pay employees a set percentage of their pre-retirement income for life. Over the last two decades, these have slowly given way to defined-contribution 401(k) accounts that individuals continue to own after they leave a job.

These plans are so popular that the AFL-CIO union opposed 401(k) reforms in 2002 in the wake of the Enron debacle because its members were concerned the reforms would impinge on their freedoms.[65] A similar transformation is beginning to take place in the health insurance sector.

The tax exclusion of employer-sponsored health insurance constitutes a large government distortion in the health care marketplace. As we've seen, at the federal level alone, this tax break is expected to total almost $140 billion in 2002.[66]

Ideally, the government would not introduce any tax distortions into consumption decisions, be it prodding individuals to purchase a house or employers to purchase health insurance for employees.

One solution is to remove these tax distortions and put all individuals on level ground when making major decisions about what mix of goods and services to purchase and consume. But here reality must intrude: Taking away tax incentives is disruptive for individuals and industries.

If the federal tax subsidy to employers were eliminated, MIT economist Jonathan Gruber estimates that 22 million Americans would lose their employer-provided coverage, a 50- percent boost in the numbers of US residents who are uninsured.[67]

We must bow to reality and work within the framework of the existing system. The goal must be to implement reforms that increase affordability. Two reforms that would achieve this are Association Health Plans and extending a full tax break to individuals who purchase health insurance.

Association Health Plans, which President Bush endorsed in his 2003 State of the Union Address, would allow large, non-employer based groups, such as lodges, trade associations, and religious organizations, to sponsor group health plans. In addition, small employers could band together to form large groups and secure lower premiums. Extending full deductibility to individual health insurance purchases, another reform that President Bush endorsed, would make such plans more affordable.

CHAPTER NINE:
So What is the Solution?

The solutions to the problems with the US health care system could be improved enormously by extending favorable tax treatment to individuals and families *regardless* of whether or not they have employment-based health insurance. This removes the bias towards job-based insurance, and makes health insurance more attractive to individual purchasers.

Government, after all, is already heavily involved in subsidizing health care. Of the nation's health care bill, valued at $1.42 trillion in 2001, the share that was financed by taxes, either through government programs or through the tax exclusion for employer-sponsored insurance, is estimated to be close to 56 percent,[68] or roughly $850 billion in 2001.

At this point, the question is no longer whether governments should subsidize the purchase of health insurance, but how?

Dr. Stuart Butler of the Heritage Foundation has fleshed out the details of a remedy. His idea is to transform gradually the tax exclusion into a refundable tax credit that can be used by all to purchase any type of insurance policy.[69] Employees could continue to receive health insurance through their employers if they wished; and for those people, the shift from the tax exclusion to a refundable tax credit would occur gradually.

For Americans without employer-sponsored insurance, however, the new refundable tax credit would provide a significant new subsidy, allowing them to purchase a policy on their own or by joining a group to purchase a group insurance policy. And by providing a limited subsidy, the tax credit would also have the effect of making people more prudent shoppers of health insurance. There would no longer be an incentive to purchase prepaid medicine, which would reduce costs by reducing unnecessary, overuse of health care.

Most important to American consumers, they would have the power to choose their own doctor and facilities.

Chapter Ten:
How Did Medicare/Medicaid Get So Big?

"Medicare is the worst health coverage that money can't even buy. If a company tried to sell it, the state insurance department would shut it down."
—Mike Leone, financial planner, Leone Financial Services

The irrationalities of the private insurance market are matched by serious problems in the public sector. Americans need not look to Canada to see the rationing and waiting lines that compulsory government health insurance can create. Medicare and Medicaid are bringing the same ills that afflict Canada to the US elderly and poor.[70]

As if this were not bad enough, Medicare is the platform that advocates of government health care hope to use in order to expand government coverage to the entire US population. "The answer is a single-payer system that covers everyone and more efficiently uses the resources we allocate to health care," writes the former editor of the *New England Journal of Medicine* and current lecturer at Harvard medical school, Marcia Angell. "This is tantamount to extending Medicare to all Americans. Medicare is not perfect, but it provides a uniform set of benefits to nearly everyone who qualifies and it does so more efficiently than the private employment-based system."[71]

The Clinton administration sought to extend Medicare's coverage to people as young as 55.[72] It is worth, then, paying close attention to both the history and current operation of Medicare—what it means for patients, physicians, and taxpayers—in order to develop a fully informed view of what nationalized health care would mean for the United States.

Far from showcasing the virtues of government health insurance, the Medicare experience exhibits its problems, including an inflexible and inadequate benefit package, inability to control spending, and an increasingly uncertain, unfair, and burdensome set of regulations on providers.

Medicare for the elderly and Medicaid for the poor were the fruits of 60 years of political efforts, culminating in the passage of the Mills Medicare Act in 1965. The act was also meant to be the first significant step on a road that would end in universal government health insurance.

The Socialist party first proposed government provision of sickness insurance in 1904. Theodore Roosevelt, running for president as a progressive, endorsed government-funded hospital insurance in 1912, a period in which there was much academic and policy agitation for the United States to follow Western Europe's lead and get the government involved in health care.[73]

After World War I and the Russian Revolution, the German and Russian models became much more controversial. In 1935, a line in the Social Security Act authorizing the Social Security Board to study national health insurance caused an uproar.[74] That didn't stop some in Congress from pushing for nationalized insurance. Each year from 1939 to 1950 there were efforts to pass national health insurance legislation. After a large push and equally large failure in 1950, President Harry Truman and health insurance advocates shifted to an incremental approach.[75]

They realized that if they got seniors—a sympathetic and politically potent constituency—covered first, they could build from there. This "foot in the door" approach, as one advocate characterized it,[76] met with success a decade later in 1960, when Congress passed the Kerr-Mills bill, which established a federal and state program to extend taxpayer-financed medical insurance to low-income seniors.

Five years later, legislators passed the Mills Medicare Act, often characterized as a three-layer cake. The first layer, Medicare Part A, paid for some hospital expenses and was to be funded by a payroll tax and a trust fund. The second was Medicare Part B, which paid for physician services and was to be funded by a combination of premiums and general tax revenue. The final layer was Medicaid, a federal and state program to pay for hospital and physician services for poor Americans. This third layer was supported by organized medicine, since it meant only new funding for new patients.

Today, all three layers of the Medicare/Medicaid cake are beginning to collapse. In March 2004, the Medicare board of trustees warned that the hospital insurance program's trust fund might be empty by the end of the next decade. The trustees warned that, "The financial status of the fund has deteriorated significantly, with asset exhaustion projected to occur in 2019 under current law compared to 2026 in last year's report."[77] As insurance, certainly, these programs leave much to be desired.

Sound insurance, as noted earlier, insures against unplanned expenses too burdensome to pay out of pocket. Yet Medicare's hospital insurance has significant co-payments for the seriously ill, and doesn't cover any expenses after 150 days in the hospital. Medicare Part B, although costly to the taxpayers at $154 billion in 2003, and bureaucratically brutal on physicians with its thousands of billing codes, doesn't offer dental or eye care.

Sixty percent of seniors had private health insurance before Medicare's birth in 1965.[78] While Medicare decimated this private market, it didn't do away with the need for specialized insurance.

In 1999, more than 25 percent of seniors had private Medigap insurance, supplemental private insurance that pays for deductibles that Medicare does not cover and emergency medical expenses abroad.[79] Still, this doesn't seem to limit health care expenses. By 1987, seniors devoted the same proportion of their income to health care as they had before Medicare was created.[80] In 1999, the average Medicare beneficiary over age 65 was projected to spend $2,430 of his own money, or 19 percent of income, on health care.[81]

> *Some 110,000 pages of regulations—six times as many as the very complex US tax code—govern what is or is not covered by Medicare. Even then, decisions often come down to what a bureaucrat working for a local payment contractor thinks is proper.*

Nor are the benefits universal, as Angell maintains.

"Whether Medicare will pay for, or consider covered, the same medical service for a patient may depend on which side of the road, or which side of the river, that patient lives," says health care lawyer Timothy Blanchard. "Consider this analogy: If (Medicare) were responsible for interstate highways, we would have a national speed limit that went something like 'reasonable and necessary; fast enough but not too fast,' with authority delegated to each state to figure out what that meant."[82]

While Medicare doesn't have a standard for medically necessary care, that doesn't stop bureaucrats from attempting to figure it out on a case-by-case basis. Nor does it stop the bureaucrats from punishing doctors when Medicare's payment contractors feel the doctors have violated the rules.

Bureaucratic control

Here, perhaps, is the greatest lesson in the unintended consequences of social engineering. The day before President Lyndon Johnson signed Medicare into law, the president assured representatives of the American Medical Association that the new program would *not* interfere in the doctor-patient relationship. Today, Medicare routinely inserts itself between doctors and patients, even when patients aren't aware of it. It second guesses doctors and binds them in red tape. What it decides it will or won't pay for often determines the care that seniors receive.

"There's a blatant way, of course, that the Medicare bureaucracy, or HCFA (now Centers for Medicare & Medicaid Services), controls what I do," says Dr. William G. Plested, a thoracic and cardiovascular surgeon and an AMA trustee. "And that's by covering or not covering a particular service or operation."[83]

Criminal diagnosis

Sometimes Medicare's rules put physicians at risk of committing what the bureaucracy considers fraud. Dr. Plested notes, for example, that Medicare won't pay for screening evaluations for elderly individuals with cardiovascular disease. "In order for me to get that patient covered for a thorough screening evaluation, I must state that I think the patient has heart disease," says Dr. Plested. "I am then at risk of being charged with fraud and abuse, saying that I think he has something just so he can be protected from something that can be easily found in a pre-operative evaluation."[84]

The worry of being prosecuted for fraud and abuse is not an idle one. In 1999, HCFA administrator Nancy-Ann DeParle announced the discovery of $12.6 billion in improper Medicare payments, and promised to crack down on it. The government has been doing so by rewarding seniors who snitch on their doctors with 30 percent of the recovered funds.

"It's called whistle-blowing for fun and profit," says attorney Robert Charrow.[85] (Participating seniors, however, might be surprised that these investigations open their private medical files to public scrutiny.)

While there are certainly cases of fraud, there is little evidence to suggest that it's close to the $12.6 billion figure DeParle claimed. The preponderance of these costs, it seems, are billing errors, most of which are random and therefore may net out to much less than the full amount. It's also easy to see how doctors could make an error, given the complexity of the system.

Administration on the cheap?

Single-payer advocates like Angell often claim that Medicare is efficient. It only spends 2 percent of revenues on overhead—they

---

The Medicare system has over 7,000 billing codes. "You know you're in trouble in medicine today when there's a code not only for flatulence, but one for the guy standing downwind as well," said Dr. Lawrence Huntoon, a neurologist and president of the American Association of Physicians and Surgeons. "There's a code for injury due to legal intervention by gas, a code for injury from being pecked by a bird, a code for injury from prolonged weightlessness, and a code for injury due to a fall from a spacecraft, flagpole, or commode. There's even a code for a person sucked into a jet engine."
(Source: Grace-Marie Arnett et al., "How Medicare Paperwork Abuses Doctors and Harms Patients," p. 7.)

---

are fond of citing—compared to figures as high as 20 percent for managed-care plans.

This figure is misleading because it fails to account for the costs that the system transfers to hospitals and physicians such as Huntoon, who spends half of his time dealing with the Medicare bureaucracy. It's as if the IRS claimed the costs of our complicated tax code were limited to the agency's processing costs, neglecting the hours that individuals and companies must spend complying with the law.

A study by the consulting firm PricewaterhouseCoopers found that for every hour hospital physicians devote to caring for a Medicare patient, hospital administrators spend 30 minutes dealing with Medicare paperwork.[86] The ratio of time on patients to time on paperwork jumps to one to one for emergency room care.[87]

Health care attorney Jonathan Emord reports that the solo and small group practices he represents spend anywhere from a quarter to half of their time on Medicare paperwork.[88]

One effect is to force physicians to join ever-larger practices to spread out the administrative costs more efficiently over a larger patient base. But even here, the figures can be staggering.

According to *Physicians Management*, an industry journal, a group practice of 284 physicians spent $130,000 to $195,000 each month just on the file dictation services required to comply with Medicare's regulations.[89]

Missing the mark

Medicare's legislative backers projected the hospital program would cost $9 billion in 1990. It actually cost $66 billion in 1990.[90] Last year, the combined spending for Medicare Parts A and B was $245 billion.

Medicare has decided that stroke victims who are released to nursing homes aren't worth the effort or cost of extensive physical rehabilitation, Dr. Huntoon notes, and must satisfy themselves with whatever the facility provides. And if they disagree, there's little they can do about it. Under Medicare regulations, they aren't allowed to pay providers extra money for better care. (Source: Arnett et al., "How Medicare Paperwork Abuses Doctors and Harms Patients," p. 5.)

The government's effort to control costs has led to ever-increasing meddling in medical practice, harming both patients and physicians. It started, as President Lyndon Johnson promised the AMA, by reimbursing hospitals and doctors on a cost-plus basis (the costs being determined reasonable by the profession).[91] But costs soon far outstripped projections, so bureaucrats and health planners scratched their heads and came up with new, non-market ways, to control costs.

Cost-saving measures pushed hospitals to economize on care, discharge patients earlier, and in general discriminated against sicker, harder-to-serve patients. One effect, notes Goodman and Musgrave, is that fewer people died in hospitals while more died in nursing homes.[92] One effect that wasn't achieved was cost management.

From 1985 to 2001, total spending on Medicare Part A increased from $48 billion to $143 billion. Medicare Part B, the program that pays the physicians, is even more meddlesome than the Hospital Insurance with its 7,000 billing codes. It requires extensive and expensive record keeping. It operates under strict price controls—controls it's been ratcheting lower and lower, and controls that essentially determine the care seniors get, whether they know it or not.

Amazingly, physicians aren't even allowed to treat Medicare patients free of charge. "We decided that we were not going to charge our Medicare patients," says Dr. Joseph Marshall. "We would see them free of charge. We'd fill out the forms, and that would take care of that. I called up Medicare to confirm this. They told me that if I was to do this, I was gong to be fined and/or end up in prison. I said, 'What?' They said, 'You're not allowed to do that.'"[93]

"I love my elderly patients," says Dr. Mark H. Krotowski, a family doctor in Brooklyn, New York. "But they are very sick. They need a lot of attention, a lot of medications, and a lot of time. Medicare reimbursement has not kept up with inflation or the cost of providing care to the elderly." (Source: Robert Pear, "Doctors Shunning Patients with Medicare," New York Times, March 17, 2002.

Limited access

With the government having cut physician fees 5.4 percent in 2002, an increasing number of physicians are choosing to limit how many Medicare patients they will see.

According to the American Academy of Family Physicians, 17 percent of family doctors are refusing to take new Medicare patients.[94]

One clinic in Kirkland, Washington, that Dr. Paul E. Buehrens directs, is among the 17 percent of Medicare *refusniks*. Medicare cut Dr. Buehrens a check for $60 for an office visit, $40 less than the $100 it costs a doctor in his clinic to see the patient. Says Dr. Buehrens, "Medicare is almost charity care."[95]

CHAPTER ELEVEN:
What About the Condition
of Our Seniors?

No demographic group is more politically powerful than American senior citizens, and no demographic group makes greater use of the health care system and the products of the pharmaceutical industry. Their economic clout has increased over time.

In 1969, one in four seniors lived in poverty. That fell to one in eight by 1999, and fewer than one in 10 by 2002.[96] (Even these figures overstate the current poverty rate among seniors. They measure annual income but ignore stocks of wealth accumulated in such things as houses and retirement accounts. In 2001, half of US seniors were worth more than $176,000.)[97] In contrast, the poverty rate for Americans under the age of 18 stood at 16 percent in 2002. One in 10 adults under the age of 65 lives in poverty.[98]

"Seniors did have increased medical expenses," notes *Business Week* writer Margaret Popper. "But that was offset by income gains."[99] Despite their relative affluence, seniors get more legislative attention than the poor of all ages.

Seniors, stuck with a 1960s government benefit package, initially warmed up to managed care, which provided a way to gain access to services Medicare wouldn't cover, such as prescription drugs and eye care, often for less out-of-pocket expense. In exchange for giving up some freedom of choice in doctors, seniors got additional services, a bargain that millions were pleased to strike. In 1990, three million seniors had signed up for managed care. By the end of the decade, the number had climbed to 6.3 million seniors.[100]

Surveys showed that seniors like their Medicare HMOs, especially when compared to the traditional system.[101] Yet this system soon started to unravel. The money the government was willing to pay for senior care, managed-care companies complained, was insufficient to provide quality care and expanded services. Managed-care companies started to drop Medicare contracts, affecting hundreds of thousands of seniors each year.

By 2003, 2.4 million seniors had been involuntarily dropped from their Medicare HMO.[102] Many found themselves being pushed back into the limited, and yet still expensive, traditional Medicare program. "It totally destroys the continuity of medical care," complains Betty Schmidt, a California senior whose HMO left the Medicare program.[103]

More recently, the government has increased the money it will pay to HMOs for Medicare patients and companies are again actively soliciting business. How long this will last is anyone's guess.

CHAPTER TWELVE:
What's Wrong with Prescription-drug Coverage for Seniors?

Until 2006, Medicare won't pay for prescription drugs consumed by patients at home. Even in 2006, seniors may be surprised at what the new prescription drug benefit covers. The benefit is a confusing jumble that few would purchase in the private market.

For an estimated premium of $35 a month, a senior faces an annual deductible of $250 before the cost of any drugs will be covered. The benefit will then pay 75 percent of purchases from $250 to $2,250, then nothing at all until the beneficiary has purchased $5,100 of product. At that point, a senior will have spent $420 on the premium and $3,600 on drugs.

In other words, it operates like a prescription drug plan with a $4,000 deductible!

Even before 2006, Medicare does, however, purchase prescription drugs for seniors who are being treated in hospitals. Low-income seniors can receive coverage for pharmaceuticals through Medicaid. More than 1.5 million seniors receive subsidies for drug purchases from state and local programs operated in 30 states.[104]

Like everything about Medicare and Medicaid, the drug program operates on top-down mandates and orders. In 1990, Congress passed a law mandating that pharmaceutical companies give

Medicaid purchasers a 15.1 percent discount off the average wholesale price of brand-name drugs.

Even with this deep discount, total costs to the government budget continued to increase. The problem in the Medicaid program is not the price at which governments purchase the drugs, but the artificially low price at which beneficiaries get them. Facing only small co-payments regardless of how expensive the drugs, consumers have no incentive to shop for lower-priced alternatives.

Yet instead of restructuring the program to put consumer self-interest to work, governments have attempted to solve the problem of heavy-handed regulation with even more regulation. And when this doesn't work, state attorneys general have turned to that most American of solutions—self-interested, profit-seeking trial lawyers.

On average, people who are 65 and over spend less on pharmaceuticals ($884 per person in 2001) than they do on entertainment ($1,067 per person in 2001).
(Source: US Department of Labor, Bureau of Labor Statistics, Consumer Expenditure Survey, 2001, Table 3.)

Largely due to Medicaid's drain on state budgets, prescription drugs have become a hot issue at the state level. In 2002, more than 180 bills dealing with pharmaceuticals were considered by state legislatures.[105]

They are sure to find that whenever the tools are government mandates, the results are the same—rationing and restrictions. For example, Michigan is in the vanguard of states trying to deal with the results of the perverse incentives of Medicaid—by implementing more perverse incentives. To control its spending on drugs, Michigan has created a state-approved "formulary" of drugs that it will purchase for Medicaid patients.

Restricted formularies are clearly the future for state drug programs. Florida has a similar program and many other states are considering them. California, Florida, and New Mexico are using the formularies as a tool to extract even greater discounts from drug manufacturers. If drug manufactures don't give another "supplementary discount" over and above the 15.1 percent they are already required to grant, state bureaucrats won't include their products on state-approved lists. So much for science and best medical judgment driving medical decisions.

Despite their relative affluence, seniors are spending more money on drugs and they don't like it. It's hard to blame them. Medicare covers hospital and physician visits. It covers nursing home care in certain instances. Why should it not provide coverage for prescription drugs?

Spending on prescription drugs has been shown to reduce hospitalization and other health care expenses by several times more.[106] Thus, federal legislators have long promised seniors a Medicare prescription drug benefit. On December 8, 2003, Congress delivered with the benefit plan set to take effect in 2006.

While the availability of pharmaceuticals for seniors is good health policy, the prescription drug benefit is a dangerous new entitlement for several reasons.

It's not just the legislators who have targeted the pharmaceutical industry. Trial lawyers, fresh off of their $208 billion dollar payday from the tobacco industry, are once again joining with state attorneys general, this time to target companies that make people healthier. No fewer than 35 states are working together to use the resources of the state to sue pharmaceutical companies. While individual cases vary, the fundamental charge is that companies have defrauded the states by falsely reporting the average wholesale price, from which the mandated discounts are computed.

(Source: Andrew Caffrey, Scott Hensley, and Russell Gold, "States Go to Court in Effort to Rein in Costs of Medicine," Wall Street Journal, May 21, 2002.)

First, the Medicare program is already in extremely precarious financial shape. Medicare spending represented 2.56 percent of the nation's gross domestic product (GDP) in 2002. This figure is predicted to rise to 4.75 percent of GDP in 2030, and to continue upward to 9.05 percent of GDP in 2075.[107] Medicare (and the other entitlement nightmare, social security) will crowd out other spending by the federal government. Without reform, it will ultimately lead to a Hobson's choice between massive budget deficits or substantial tax increases.

Even without a drug benefit, Medicare will consume 20 percent of federal income tax revenues in 2026. If a drug benefit that pays 25 percent of beneficiaries' drug costs were added, Medicare would consume 24 percent of income tax revenue in 2026. If the drug benefit pays 75 percent of drug costs, Medicare would consume 35 percent of income tax revenues in that year.[108] This is new spending for the government that displaces private spending. Therefore, the government will have to increase revenue to accomplish it.

Second, a Medicare prescription drug benefit would inevitably be subject to price controls, which would severely jeopardize the development of next-generation drugs. (Spending by the drug industry on research and development, R&D, is closely linked to its profits.)[109] In 2003, the pharmaceutical industry spent 33 billion in R&D.[110]

Price controls on drugs for Medicare beneficiaries will also lead to increased prices in the private sector. This was demonstrated when Medicaid, the health care program for the poor, imposed price controls on drugs. After a 1990 law mandated that Medicaid recipients get the "best price," manufacturers responded by reducing their discounts to the private sector.[111]

However, because the prescription drug benefit does not become effective until January 1, 2006, a coalition of health care organizations, including pharmaceutical companies and retail pharmacies, announced in March 2004 the establishment of a Medicare-approved drug discount card. The coalition offers low-income Medicare beneficiaries immediate assistance in obtaining prescription medicines through the Centers for Medicare and Medicaid Services (CMS). The new card program is called the U Share Prescription Drug Discount Card ("U Share Card") and it went into effect in June 2004. It is sponsored and managed by United Health Group.

This new program is designed to provide Medicare beneficiaries with access to prescription drugs while at the same time maintaining the integrity of the patient-physician and patient-pharmacist relationships that are at the heart of the US health care delivery system. Such initiatives are important steps in preserving the viability of the US pharmaceutical industry.

CHAPTER THIRTEEN:
Is There a Solution for Seniors?

The answer for seniors, as it is for the working insured and the uninsured, is to redirect the existing government subsidy to provide consumers with a choice of privately-run health-insurance plans. Americans under the age of 65 do not have to ask whether drug benefits will be part of their health plan. Private sector health plans long ago saw the value of prescription drugs for providing cost-effective care and integrated them into their benefit offerings.

A model for providing seniors with a choice of health plans already exists—Congress, congressional staff, and nearly all employees of the federal government use it. This system is known as the Federal Employees Health Benefits Program (FEHBP).

The FEHBP offers a menu of insurance plans to federal employees. There are 12 national fee-for-service insurance plans available nationwide to any federal employee. Furthermore, there are six national fee-for-service plans that enroll certain categories of federal workers. In addition, HMOs operate in many metropolitan areas.

The result is that the FEHBP offers federal employees a much greater choice of health plans than non-federal workers receive under the employment-based health-insurance system.

A variation of a defined contribution, called "premium support" finances the FEHBP. The government contributes 75 percent of the premium for a plan, up to a maximum contribution of $2,842 for individual enrollees and $6,490 for families in 2003.[112] Federal employees must pay the difference between the premium and the government contribution. This gives employees an incentive to shop for lower-priced plans.

In a similar way, we could give seniors a wider range of choices, appropriate to their condition, while restraining costs.

One of the best kept secrets, at least from the media and policymakers who continually talk of a drug cost "crisis" for low income seniors, is that there are already programs, both sponsored by governments and private companies, that significantly subsidize this group's purchases of prescription drugs. American seniors who are retired on incomes of less than 100 percent of the poverty level and who have amassed few assets on which to live are eligible for both Medicare by virtue of their age, and Medicaid by virtue of their economic status. It is these seniors, roughly one in six, for whom paying for prescription drugs is the greatest burden.[113] Thanks to a taxpayer-supported program, they are largely relieved of this burden.

Seniors who earn too much to qualify for Medicaid but still struggle economically may be eligible for state-based drug subsidy programs. "If you're looking for relief from the high cost of prescription drugs, start with your own state," advises AARP. "Most states offer some sort of pharmacy assistance program, many of which require little or no up-front payment to join—making these plans the first option for cost conscious consumers."[114]

Thirty-four states currently sponsor plans. Seniors in Connecticut with incomes under $28,100, for example, can purchase the more generous of a month's supply of a prescription or 120 caplets for $16.25 per prescription.[115]

One-and-a-half million seniors are enrolled in a state-sponsored plan. So even before the new Medicare drug benefit started, nearly 20 percent of seniors, the poorest one in five, were receiving highly subsidized prescription drugs. And this doesn't even count what the pharmaceutical companies offer.

An administrative fee of $12 purchases a month's supply of any Eli Lilly and Co. product for lower income seniors or disabled Americans without prescription drug coverage. The same is true for Novartis products. Pfizer's fee for a month's supply is $15.[116]

The United States is a compassionate country and, as the above programs illustrate, has long been assisting its neediest citizens—those unable to support themselves—with the necessities of life.

CHAPTER FOURTEEN:
What is the Proper Role of Doctors?

The managed care revolution has been even tougher on doctors than on patients.

Accustomed to being their own boss, doctors found themselves ordered around and second-guessed by managed care companies. Doctors had successfully fought off the direct government provision of health care only to find themselves at the mercy of MBAs.

"The inability to control the way we practice medicine and deliver care to patients is the reason that physicians are leaving medicine in record numbers," a physician complained to the *New York Times*. "I can tell you that on an ordinary working day, if I didn't have a single patient to see, I would still be busy for eight or nine hours doing nothing but paperwork and phone calls that are directly related to managed care issues."[117] The result, complain doctors, is a reduction in quality—and, though they talk less about it, a reduction in income.

Pay cut

The Massachusetts Medical Society Physician Practice Environment Index shows that in the 1990s, Bay State doctors worked more hours for less money. In 1992, they had an average income of $140,000 and worked 49.5 hours a week, which dropped to an estimated $120,600 for 52.8 hours in 2000.[118]

SimpleCare, based in Renton, Washington, is enabling doctors and patients to reestablish trust in one another by removing third parties from the relationship. Doctors participating in SimpleCare agree to offer their "best price" for their services and patients agree to pay their fees at the time of service. Patients pay an annual membership fee of $20 a person or $35 a family to enroll in the system. Patients are encouraged to purchase high-deductible insurance for true medical emergencies.

In return, doctors can rid themselves of administrative staff and the time spent coding and filing insurance claims, enabling them to offer low prices for medical care. By paying a lower fee directly to the doctor at the time of service, consumers can expect more personalized attention and a higher quality of care. Some doctors charge as little as $35 for a visit.[a] "It costs less than a plumber," says Lloyd Sullivan, a self-employed stock trader from Bellingham, Washington. "It's more than fair and I couldn't be happier about it."[b]

Dr. Robert Berry of Greeneville, Tennessee, a SimpleCare member, even calls his practice the PATMOS Emergiclinic, the acronym standing for "Payment At Time Of Service." He publishes his fees and reports that many of his patients are uninsured.

Even if they don't join a group such as SimpleCare, many doctors are, nevertheless, abandoning HMOs and preferred provider contracts. A recent survey by the University of California, San Francisco found that only 58 percent of doctors in California are accepting new HMO patients.[c]

(Sources: [a]"Reimbursement: Doctor's group expands patient payment system," Managed Health care Info, April 22, 2002. [b]Quoted in "Reimbursement: Doctor's group expands..." [c]Sabin Russell, "Doctors in state fleeing HMOs," San Francisco Chronicle, February 9, 2003.

According to a recent survey of physicians published in the *New England Journal of Medicine*, 24 percent of primary-care doctors and 38 percent of specialists reported they were uncomfortable with the amount of care that primary-care physicians are expected to provide their patients before sending them to a specialist.[119]

"I couldn't stand it anymore—the day was an absolute treadmill," complains Dr. Bernard Kaminetsky, who set up a specialized practice that offers personalized services for a substantial fee. "I wanted to devote more time to patients. I wanted to enjoy practicing."[120]

Studies may not show that managed care diminishes the quality of care. But doctors are convinced it does. A Kaiser/Harvard survey found that seven in 10 doctors believe that the quality of care has *decreased*. In fact, almost half of doctors admit to manipulating the system by exaggerating their patients' symptoms to get their patients the care they need.[121] The managed care revolution also did indisputable damage to the doctor-patient relationship. Shifting decisions back to individuals and families would have a beneficial effect on relations between patients and doctors. To this end, many doctors have already taken action by dropping their third-party insurance contracts. Some new organizations have arisen to help them.

Tender loving care

Some doctors, rather than eliminate third parties and lower their fees, have begun boutique or "concierge" medical practices that cater to individuals willing to pay a premium for their services. The rapid growth of these services reveals the hunger for a restoration of the doctor-patient relationship.

Empowering individual patients to make their own health care choices would be a boon to doctors, giving them more autonomy to make the best medical decisions. It would restore the potential for increasing income. But its greatest benefits would be felt in the heart—the ability to have a relationship with patients based on trust.

CHAPTER FIFTEEN:
What's the Best Role
for Insurance Companies?

The promise of HMOs, which takes decisions out of the hands of doctors and patients and puts them in the hands of expert planners, stayed in favor for some time. President Bill Clinton's 1993 plan to remake the entire US health care system centered on HMOs. But the fascination could not last. President Clinton's plan failed and its regional health alliances, that would have put all US health care under government control, disappeared, hopefully forever. However, the spirit of the Clinton plan remained, and the distorted health care market soon accomplished one company at a time what President Clinton would have done in one fell swoop: Companies traded unaffordable indemnity medical insurance plans for managed care.

From 1993 to 2001, enrollment in managed care, broadly defined as HMOs, PPOs, and point-of-service plans, increased from 52 percent to 92 percent of employees.[122] As noted earlier, patients and doctors soon chafed under the restrictions. Again, the call went out for the government to do something, and it responded at all levels.

States were the first to regulate managed care, passing so-called "patients' bills of rights" that restricted the most onerous practices of HMOs. Doctors were particularly eager to open up the networks with "any willing provider" legislation to force insurance companies to pay their fees to any doctor willing to provide services.

Other popular provisions sought included outside review boards to second-guess decisions made by insurance company bureaucrats. Managed care liability laws allowed beneficiaries to sue their plan. By late summer 2001, nine states had passed such liability laws: Arizona (2000), California (1999), Georgia (1999), Maine (1999), New Jersey (2001), Oklahoma (2000), Texas (1997), Washington (2000), and West Virginia (2001).[123]

It wasn't long before the federal government got into the game, with legislators offering their own patients' bill of rights. As it stands now, the lead bill is sponsored by Democratic Senator Edward M. Kennedy from Massachusetts, an effective legislator committed to national health insurance. However, Senator Kennedy's proposal is a Pandora's box of unintended consequences. (At this writing, the bill is not expected to become law in this Congress, though it will likely reemerge.)

In the economic boom of the late 1990s, the perceived problem in US health care shifted from the plight of the uninsured to the quality of health insurance. In the marketplace, firms responded to employee preferences by offering less restrictive PPO plans, which cost employers and employees more but allowed more freedom of choice. One result has been a return to increases in medical insurance premiums.

From spring 2000 to spring 2001, employer-sponsored health-insurance premiums jumped 11 percent, the largest increase since 1992.[124] Medical insurance premiums for federal employees and their families increased by 13.3 percent in 2002.[125] As we saw earlier, this trend is continuing, with the Kaiser Family Foundation reporting that health care premiums for families in employer-sponsored plans soared 13.9 percent in 2003, the third year of double-digit growth.

Factors driving the increases, according to the *Wall Street Journal*, include "a rapidly rising pharmaceutical bill," "stronger medical organizations that are better able to extract bigger pay increases from insurers," and "a continuing backlash against the main principles of managed care, such as restrictions on choice and mandatory referrals."[126]

So what is the best role for insurance companies? They can sort out their competitive advantages to the benefit of the consumer—but only if we first change the tax code so that the incentive for buying health care is transferred from the workplace to the individual. Under this plan, people would still join groups to buy health care, but they would do it through myriad, voluntary arrangements. In this way, companies can keep costs down by relying on market forces and competition.

Individuals could count on greater choice. Doctors could count on greater freedom to rely on their judgment. And insurance companies could be free of much of the rancor and politics of the present arrangement.

Chapter Sixteen:
Why Not Crack Down on Greedy Pharmaceutical Companies?

No one complains of automobile price inflation if people spend more of their income on vehicles because they purchase more vehicles per household, or buy a fully loaded SUV instead of a compact car. But then people don't expect someone else to buy their cars for them. They do expect third parties to buy their drugs, and those third parties often care more about the total amount they spend on drugs, rather than the value they deliver to individuals.

Pharmaceutical companies are also easy targets because they are profitable and they aggressively market their products on television. "Big drug companies are putting more money into advertising and promotion than they are into research and development," declared presidential candidate Al Gore in 2000. This is completely false but that fact hasn't stopped other politicians from repeating him.

In 2001, the industry spent $19.1 billion on all promotional activities. Of this amount, only 14 percent was for direct-to-consumer advertising, while 55 percent was for handing out free product samples for doctors to give to their patients.

By comparison, as previously mentioned, the industry spent $33 billion on R&D in 2003. Gore's narrative depicted an evil industry victimizing a poor citizenry. His campaign story of 79-year-old Winifred Skinner, a former auto-worker who supposedly had to walk Iowa's highways collecting cans to pay her $250-a-month bill for blood pressure and heart medications, turned out to be something of a ruse.[127]

The attack on the pharmaceutical industry was absurd in other ways. People don't normally attack the institutions that provide them with a better quality of life. Few people curse car companies for charging high prices for their products in order to make a profit.

Cheap pills

Actually, pharmaceuticals are comparatively inexpensive. Americans as a whole spend one percent of their income on drugs, according to the Bureau of Labor Statistics.[128] Seniors over age 65 spend three percent of their income on drugs, less than the amount they spend on entertainment.[129]

In fact, Americans spend less on prescription drugs than they do on alcohol, tobacco, and admission fees to concerts, movies, and cultural and sporting events. "You could just as easily say that football was the problem," says Princeton economist Uwe Reinhardt.[130] Nor is spending on drugs as a share of total health spending significantly above historical levels. In 1960, Americans spent 10 percent of their health care dollars on pharmaceuticals. This declined to five percent in the 1980s, and only now has risen back up to the 10-percent level.[131]

By most standards, modern drugs ought to be seen as an extraordinary value. Given a choice between the medicine cabinet of 1970 or 2002, few would take the past over the present. Per-person spending on drugs was only $110 in 1970. Today it exceeds $400, but the benefits are much greater.

Powerful medicine

In 1988, Congress added prescription coverage to Medicare as part of the Medicare Catastrophic Coverage Act. When the costs of the act became clear—and, more important, it became clear that seniors would be forced to pay for all of the increased costs—senior citizens rebelled and Congress repealed the act in short order.[132]

Meanwhile, seniors—indeed, all Americans—have increased their third-party coverage of prescription drugs. In 1990, 59 percent of pharmaceutical spending in the United States was out-of-pocket spending by individuals.[133] By 2002, out-of-pocket drug spending had dropped to only 30 percent. Insurance covered 48 percent and governments paid for the remaining 22 percent.[134] Although Medicare still provides no coverage for outpatient prescription drugs, roughly two-thirds of seniors receive drug coverage from another source.

Pfizer's Neal A. Masia: "In 1970, there were no pills to treat Alzheimer's Disease or impotence; no statin drugs to lower cholesterol; no proton pump inhibitors to treat ulcers or GERD; no advanced antihistamines to treat allergies and congestion; no revolutionary products to treat depression and anxiety; and so on."
(Source: Neal A. Masia, "Pharmaceutical Innovation: Lowering the Price of Good Health," Economic Realities in Health Care Policy, vol. 2, issue 2 (April 2002).)

For the large health plans responsible for the comprehensive care of individuals, it's not hard for them to see that pharmaceuticals are powerful medicine indeed. By using the best and latest drugs, patients enjoy better quality of life and often avoid invasive procedures.

In 1998, WellPoint Health Networks, a large health insurer, noticed a growing trend of emergency room hospitalizations for asthma patients—a trend that hurt the company as well as the patients. It worked with a pharmaceutical consultant to set up a program to train patients to use inhalers more effectively. "We found that even though drug costs went up about 20 percent, hospital admissions and emergency room visits went down by 80 percent—and overall costs by 48 percent," stated Kathleen A. Johnson, the University of Southern California pharmaceutical economist who helped develop the program.[135]

For some reason, government is often oblivious to this benefit-cost dynamic. Politicians and bureaucrats tend to only look at drug spending in searching for ways to hold down costs. States that administer the Medicaid program for low-income Americans complain that pharmaceutical spending is breaking state budgets. Their worries are misplaced.

The real problem is a program that rejects consumer empowerment in favor of price controls and bureaucracy. There is a disconnection between who pays for care and who benefits from it. Pharmaceuticals often improve the quality of life for patients, especially when compared to other options, but state governments look at the line items and only see that drug spending is growing.

In a year-long disease management program, Humana Hospitals studied 1,100 congestive heart patients. While its pharmacy costs increased by 60 percent, it reduced hospital costs by 78 percent, resulting in net savings of $9.3 million. The use of pharmaceuticals also saved lives. The expected death rate dropped from one in four patients to one in 10. (Source: Ronald Bailey, "Goddam the Pusher Man,"Reason, April 2001.)

Preventing progress

By cracking down on the ability of pharmaceutical companies to earn profits on given drugs, state bureaucrats put at risk what close observers of the pharmaceutical industry call "the third revolution." This revolution, according to scholar John Calfee, combines all the elements of our modern market economy, prolific science, powerful computers, venture capital, flexible labor markets, and creative advertising and marketing, to bring a new wave of wonder medicines to this world.[136] This revolution is occurring in a few places and driven by identifiable factors, most notably the profit motive. But the entire world stands to benefit from drugs and therapies that can save lives and reduce suffering. Once they are developed in the US, they can be enjoyed around the world.

A whole generation of lifestyle products has also come to market that improves people's lives in myriad ways. These products treat allergies, pain, mild obesity, depression, and even hair loss.[137] Science writer Ronald Bailey, for example, credits a drug with saving his marriage. The drug is not Viagra. It's Pfizer's Zyrtec, a one-pill-a-day, non- drowsy antihistamine that allows him to coexist with his wife's cats. "A month's supply costs $66.25 at my local pharmacy," writes Bailey. "But what price love?"[138]

During the 1990s, the pharmaceutical industry made almost 400 new drugs available to consumers, which either provided a treatment where none existed before or significantly improved on existing drugs.[139] The United States is clearly the arena for this revolution. Since 1980, half of the new drugs available have been developed and produced in the United States. The top ten sellers are also US products.[140] Such creativity is not something that government planners can produce or replace if regulation destroys the right mix of incentives and actors.

Twenty-three drugs accounted for half of the increased drug spending in 2000. These drugs—including Vioxx and Celebrex for arthritis, Lipitor for cholesterol, and Prevacid for heartburn—greatly enhance the quality of life.

According to a study by the National Institute for Health Care Management Research and Educational Foundation, 42 percent of the increased spending in 2000 was due to an increase in the number of prescriptions purchased, and 36 percent was from a shift to more expensive— and presumably more effective— prescriptions. Yet price increases for existing drugs accounted for only 22 percent of the increase in total spending. (Source: "Prescription Spending Up 18% in 2000; Fifth Straight Year of Increases," Reuters Health, May 4, 2001.)

The right mix

These innovations can only come from profit-seeking corporations working in market environments that are increasingly rare in the world. Policymakers have failed to catch up to the ground-breaking improvements of this third revolution.

Increased spending on drugs should be viewed as a sign of progress, not of failure.

Yet attention remains focused on drug prices. Numerous researchers have studied this issue, relying on a variety of sources. What they've repeatedly found is that price increases are not the main driver of drug spending. Instead, spending increases are driven largely by two factors—increased use of existing drugs, and spending on new prescription drugs.

Single-entry bookkeeping

Some regulators are oblivious to the fact that many drugs reduce the total cost of treating diseases. This became clear in October 2000 when the New Hampshire Medicaid program limited the number of prescriptions for which it would pay. The bureaucrats may have saved some money in their pharmaceutical budget line, but the practical effect was to put chronically ill elderly patients in the admission line for nursing homes. Their rate of admission doubled.[141]

The clot-busters for stroke victims save four times as much as they cost.[142] For schizophrenia patients and their families, $4,500 a year may seem like a lot to spend on medications. But this

Since the first protease inhibitor for HIV-patients was approved in 1996, the mortality rate for HIV/AIDS has dropped in the US by 75 percent.[a] And the drugs have saved money while doing so. One study documented a $433 per-patient, per-month savings for HIV-infected patients after the introduction of an antiretroviral cocktail.[b] (Sources: [a]Lee Gillespie-White, "Patent Protection & Patients' Access to HIV/AIDS Drugs in Sub-Saharan Africa," Fraser Forum (February 2001): 12. [b]S.A. Bozzette et al. "Expenditures for the Care of HIV-Infected Patients in the Era of Highly Active Antiretroviral Therapy," New England Journal of Medicine, vol. 344, no. 11 (March 15, 2001): 817-819.)

expense not only purchases freedom, it saves $73,000 a year in the cost of institutional care.[143]

The stomach-acid-blocking Tagamet and Zantac have saved thousands of individuals from the pain and expense of surgeries for peptic ulcers. Ronald Bailey notes that in 1977, the first year such drugs appeared, 97,000 Americans endured such surgeries. By 1993 a mere 19,000 had this operation, even though the population had increased by more than 37.5 million.[144]

According to research by Columbia University professor Frank Lichtenberg, every $1 of increased spending on newer pharmaceuticals reduces other health care expenditures by an average of $7.17.[145] In Canada, a recent study found that the best way to reduce waiting times for surgery would be for government to spend more money on drugs.[146] That's just the money saved within the confines of the health care system. Yet there are significant costs of sickness that fall outside of the health care system—the costs paid by individuals in diminished quality of life, and by employers in lost productivity.

Migraine headaches, for example, cost health care payers $1 billion. It is estimated that their effects cost American employers 13 times that much.[147] Pharmaceutical companies introduced a new class of medicines to treat migraines in 1993. A 1999 study showed that individuals taking these drugs had only half the absenteeism of workers who took a placebo. Employers experienced a productivity increase from the drugs of $850 per worker, half of it stemming from fewer missed days and the other half attributable to the effects of workers feeling better on the job.[148]

In a high-profile ABC News Special in May 2002, anchor Peter Jennings told viewers that pharmaceutical manufacturers are the most profitable industry in the country, presumably basing this claim on annual industry rankings by *Fortune* magazine.[149] According to *Fortune*, the top 14 pharmaceutical companies had a median profit as a percentage of revenue of 18 percent, which wasn't out of line with other US industries. The median profit for commercial banking and savings institutions, for example, was only slightly lower at 14 percent.[150]

In judging the profits of "greedy" pharmaceuticals, few report that profits vary between individual companies, and from year to year for each company. In 2001, for example, Amgen was the most profitable drug company with a 28 percent return on revenue.[151] In 2002, however, it had losses of $1.4 billion, ranking it dead last among the pharmaceutical companies.[152] In 2001, Pharmacia and Abbott Laboratories each earned a 7 percent return on revenue, but in 2002, Pharmacia's profit was only 4 percent while Abbott's was 16 percent. Meanwhile, Genzyme suffered losses in both years, with a -9 percent return in 2001 and a -1 percent return in 2002.[153]

By comparison, Coca-Cola enjoyed 20 percent and 16 percent returns in 2001 and 2002, respectively. A Coke tastes great, but as policy analyst Merrill Matthews has commented, "Coca-Cola never saved a life."[154]

Interestingly, Barr Laboratories, a generic drug maker, made the list of the *Fortune* 1000 companies in 2002. Its profits were 18 percent of revenue, which was better than many of the research drug companies on the list. This raises another flag with regard to profits: simple measures of profitability fail to take into account the risk involved in earning that return.

Paying for progress

Research drug companies spent $33 billion on research and development in 2003, with no guarantee of a return on investment. Pharmaceutical companies spend an average of $897 million to develop a new drug, including studies conducted after receiving regulatory approval for the drug.[155] The process commonly takes between 12 and 15 years.[156]

Barr Laboratories, meanwhile, makes no such investment. With its low-risk profile, Barr's 18 percent return signals to investors that generics are a better bet than a research drug company, even when both companies have similar returns.

In fact, there is some reason to worry that R&D has become riskier. In 2001, the industry spent three times more on research than what it spent a decade earlier, yet is producing fewer drugs.[157] Bristol-Myers Squibb has sunk $16.5 billion into R&D since 1990 and, as of April 2002, didn't have a single new product to show for it.[158]

For every product a company brings to market, it abandons scores of others. Only one in five prospective drugs that enters clinical trials emerges as a viable product.[159] And only three out of 10 drugs that make it to market return what is invested in them.[160]

The products we enjoy today are the results of research costs that were incurred years ago. Still, current research budgets must be directly related to expected future profits.[161] Innovative drugs in the next decade depend on research that is done now. Any threat to current profits is a direct threat to future products—and potentially, a threat to human health and lives.

Between 1981 and 1991, the industry's annual increase in R&D spending averaged 11 percent, and had never dropped below seven percent. When President Clinton proposed price controls for pharmaceuticals in 1994 as part of his Health Security Act, annual growth in R&D dropped to three percent. It was four percent in 1995, and only recovered in subsequent years. (Source: Calfee, Prices, Markets, and the Pharmaceutical Revolution, p. 46.)

As *Wall Street Journal* columnist Holman W. Jenkins, Jr. notes, drugs ought to be the easiest sector of the health care system in which to control costs. Unlike most health services, they are a quantifiable product, their effects and relative costs easily studied, and they exist in a national market.

The main problem with drugs is that a functional market has been distorted by a dysfunctional payment system. Writes Jenkins, "How does a system with a vast tax subsidy to channel every ache and pain through the insurance system make sure consumers are careful about bringing cost and benefit into balance?"[162]

As mentioned previously, in May 2002, ABC News anchor Peter Jennings, a Canadian by birth, hosted an investigative special on the pharmaceutical industry. The overriding theme of the special was, as Jenkins notes, "Anything bad about the drug industry must be true and anything true must be bad."[163]

Jennings' report was replete with non-sequiturs and contradictions. Specifically, Jennings fingered the key problem as the patent system, which supposedly grants monopolies. But the anchor also claimed that the problem was me-too drugs, which, by definition, means there is competition. Striking closer to the heart of the matter, Jenkins writes, "Obviously the problem isn't an absence of choice but a failure of patients and doctors to exercise choice based on price." That is hardly the fault of big PhRMA.[164]

CHAPTER SEVENTEEN:
How Should We Treat Pharmaceuticals?

Given their effectiveness, prescription drugs should continue to consume a greater percentage of health care expenditures. To fully benefit from these drugs without exploding health care budgets will require creative thinking.

Currently in development are 402 new medicines to fight cancer, 123 new medicines for heart disease and stroke, 83 drugs and vaccines for HIV/AIDS, and 176 new drugs for neurological diseases. Your life may depend on maintaining the viability of the free- market system to transform science into products.

With the mapping of the human genome, a future generation of drugs based upon genetic research holds tremendous promise for battling illness, improving lives, and holding down overall health costs. Yet even with all their beneficial effects, as drug costs account for a greater proportion of total health care costs, there will be continued scrutiny.

The focus, then, should not be on drug prices, but rather on how we pay for drugs.

Today, many insurance plans offer drug benefits that do not enable the most efficient use of prescriptions. Most health plans continue to use co-payments as the method of cost sharing. Co-payments are a flat dollar amount, with a typical drug benefit having, for instance, a $10 co-pay for generic drugs and a $20

Not everyone welcomes the PBM innovation. By bringing efficiencies and national scale to the drug market, they take sales away from less efficient stores. Those stores banded together and, like mohair producers at the dawn of synthetic fiber, they are working the halls of Congress and the state capitols to protect their profits by restricting competition. Their goal is to subject PBMs to state pharmacy regulations, and hence increase their costs and the cost of drugs.

The local pharmacists enjoyed their first success in 2002, when Georgia passed a law that would regulate PBMs. The particular irony is that a year earlier, the state's Medicaid program, in an effort to reduce drug costs, contracted with a PBM to try to achieve it without severe rationing. "So far, it's been successful," Marty Smith, a spokesman for the Medicaid system, told the Wall Street Journal. It won't be for long.

(Source: Russell Gold, "Drug Benefits Managers Come Under Fire, As Pharmacists Push States for Regulations," Wall Street Journal, September 5, 2001.)

co-pay for brand-name drugs. Co-pays eliminate the price differences between drugs and shield consumers from their true cost.

Co-pays became a standard part of drug-benefit design during the managed care revolution of the 1990s. However, they are not part of a rational benefits design. They exist more as an afterthought. Many on the political left believe that patients should not have to pay anything out of their own pockets for health care. Indeed, the single-payer proposal defeated by Oregon voters in 2002 imposed no co-payments or deductibles.

HMOs were also built around the idea of "improving access" to health care by removing out-of-pocket costs. Of course, when consumers face no cost for services, they will tend to greatly overuse those services. The HMOs put controls in place to counteract that inclination. Still, when something is free, there remains an overwhelming tendency to consume as much of it as possible. If there is no cost to see your doctor, why not try to schedule a visit every week? Thus HMOs, which, after all, operate in a competitive market, instituted co-pays to keep consumers from going overboard.

Now that the rationing techniques of managed care are on the decline, the flawed economic incentives of co-pays have become evident. Without strict, managed care rationing, co-pays are fueling health care cost increases.

Fortunately, the private sector is developing solutions that match the needs of consumers with the need to control costs.

Solution: Pharmacy Benefit Managers

To control pharmaceutical costs without killing the incentives that drive research, we need to allow the private sector to develop new institutions that make purchasers sensitive to price. The most pervasive institutions are Pharmacy Benefit Managers (PBMs), firms that act as brokers to supply the most cost-effective drugs to health plans.

These private firms get discounts though bulk purchases. They also study the effectiveness of drugs. PBMs work to substitute generics for name brand drugs when appropriate. By 2002, PBMs were involved in the sale of $1.2 billion worth of pharmaceuticals for 150 million Americans.[165]

Another market response to increased drug spending addresses a fundamental problem in the system. Doctors, as well as patients, often have no idea what drugs cost. One study found that 80 percent of doctors surveyed didn't know how much their patients paid for the drugs they prescribed. Four in 10 of these doctors underestimated the cost of the drugs they prescribed.[166] Certainly doctors can't prescribe based on the relative cost effectiveness of drugs if they don't know the costs.

Solution: Shorten Drug Approval Times

Successfully getting a pharmaceutical product to market is a long, expensive process. In 1964, it took 6.5 years to get a pharmaceutical product approved for sale, according to Henry I. Miller, a former FDA official and current research fellow at the Stanford-based Hoover Institution. Today, it takes roughly 15 years.[167]

This regulatory delay adds considerably to the cost of developing new treatments, and hence to the price that consumers ultimately pay. The Tufts Center for the Study of Drug Development finds that time accounts for as much as 48 percent of the clinical costs of developing some drugs.[168] Cutting regulatory review times by 25 percent, the center estimates, would shave $129 million off the cost of drug approval.[169]

Solution: Virtual Comparison Shopping

A web site, *Rxaminer.com*, is filling this void. For a fee of $10, the site supplies patients and doctors with customized reports on all the available drugs to treat a specific condition. Sometimes the best alternative is a generic drug. Other times, however, the most appropriate drug isn't the lowest priced, but one that costs a bit more.

This site can save patients up to 75 percent on the cost of their prescriptions. "It's an easy example of how you can save money in medicine and at the same time practice better medicine," Detroit cardiologist Joseph Rogers, who founded the site with his son, told the *Wall Street Journal*.[170]

Solution: Extend Over-the-Counter Status

Another potential source of savings is to explore the extension of over-the-counter status to certain drugs. In 2001, WellPoint Health Networks petitioned the FDA to switch the leading anti-allergy medicine Claritin from prescription to over-the-counter status. Claritin's manufacturer, Schering-Plough Corp., initially fought the change, but after it lost an unprecedented FDA hearing, it announced its intention to go along with the move.[171]

Claritin began selling over the counter in December 2002. By May 2003, it was selling for 95 cents per pill, or $28.50 for a full month's supply of 30 pills. Even for most insured persons, a typical doctor's visit and prescription would require a greater out-of-pocket expense.

WellPoint, meanwhile, has shed the $90 million a year that it used to pay for Claritin prescriptions and related doctor visits.[172] Furthermore, consumers who don't want to pay 95 cents per pill for Claritin can buy the generic version of Claritin, known as loratadine. Wal-itin, the version of loratadine sold by the Walgreens pharmacy chain, costs only 75 cents per pill. An independent drug store was spotted selling loratadine for as low as 35 cents per pill.[173]

Schering-Plough saw its profits for the first quarter of 2003 fall 71 percent. But Claritin had lost its 20-year patent protection anyway. Even if it were still being sold as a prescription drug, generic competition would have had much the same effect on Schering's bottom line. The switch to over-the-counter status probably did not have a significant effect.

Overall, the switch has clearly been beneficial. Price competition in the over-the-counter marketplace has lowered the cost of health care.

Solution: Consumer-Driven Health Plans

A more efficient benefit structure would expose consumers to the real prices of drugs and enable them to see the full price differences between competing drugs. These are plans that offer a competitive, cafeteria-style choice of health care options. We will soon look at these plans in greater depth.

Though it sounds politically difficult, consumer-driven health plans are already gaining acceptance in the American marketplace. As with similar solutions, we come back to a single principle—to move policymakers from thinking about how much we pay for drugs, to how we pay for them.

CHAPTER EIGHTEEN:
Why Not Just Import
Cheap Drugs?

Independent of government policy, technology is turning local pharmaceutical markets into national and even international markets. Canada's price controls certainly create arbitrage opportunities for entrepreneurs. At least one firm is making a handsome profit by charging Americans for day trips from Seattle to Canada, where busloads of people buy cheaper drugs.[174] Another group of medical entrepreneurs announced plans to open up an American-only clinic just over the Canada-US border.[175]

Mail-order and web-based cross-border drug sellers have exploded. In 2000, fewer than 20 pharmacies sold $50 million worth of pills to 40,000 US consumers, according to the Canadian International Pharmacy Association. By 2003, 140 pharmacies were selling $800 million of product to one million Americans.[176]

Politicians are paying attention. In 2000, President Clinton signed a law allowing the re-importation of pharmaceuticals from 26 countries. Clinton's own Department of Health and Human Services (HHS) refused to issue the regulations to implement it. The measure did not result in a single pill returning to the United States at a lower price.[177]

Then in July of 2002 the US Senate passed a re-importation bill, this time limiting the country through which US-produced drugs could be legally laundered to Canada.

State and local politicians, faced with budget deficits, are looking to Canadian drugs to cut the money they spend on drugs for retirees and employees. As of early 2004, 25 states and 15 localities were considering importing drugs from Canada. The governor of Minnesota established a website that directs people to Canadian pharmacies. Springfield, Massachusetts, and Montgomery, Alabama, were actually violating US law and importing drugs from Canada for their employees and retirees.

Given the lower costs, what could be wrong with re-importation? Plenty. The growth of importation schemes threatens to destroy the delicate balance of incentives that makes the United States the best—perhaps the last—place on earth for pharmaceutical innovation.

Of course, the industry's cost structure makes it an easy target for political demagogues. Overlooked by critics are the high fixed costs of research and development for pharmaceuticals—costs that are sunk before the first batch of pills makes it to the local drugstore. So a given pill might costs billions to develop, but only 20 cents to manufacture.

With R&D costs largely invisible to the public, it is hard to explain to the public that selling a 20-cent pill for, say, 25 cents would still constitute a financial disaster for pharmaceuticals.

Pricing for a profit

Also little appreciated is the role price discrimination plays in allowing pharmaceuticals to manage their cost structure. Economists call this "discriminatory pricing," but it has nothing to do with what we usually think of as discrimination. Discrimination based on race and sex, for example, is an irrational and unfair treatment of individuals. Price discrimination, on the other hand, is what airlines do when they charge business travelers higher fares than leisure travelers who book two to three weeks in advance. In a similar way, pharmaceutical firms have an incentive to charge different prices to different customers, depending on how much they are willing to pay.

Of course, one might denounce senior fares as unfair discrimination against those who pay the higher price. Yet discriminatory pricing does not make anyone worse off than they were before. In fact, by allowing more people to purchase the product, it renders consumers as a group better off. As long as demand grows, price discrimination results in net benefits for the maximum number of buyers, while allowing sellers to maximize profitability.

A simplified example illustrates this point. Suppose "Clear Skin Inc." develops and patents a pill that clears up acne and needs to be taken only once a week. It's clearly an improvement over creams and other over-the-counter products. Suppose, as well, that the company spent $100 million to develop and test the pill, but that the cost of manufacturing the medicine is only 10 cents per pill.

If Clear Skin believes it can sell 100 million pills, the company would need to earn $110 million in revenue to recoup its total costs for the drug. So if Clear Skin were to charge a uniform price to attain that revenue, it would price the pill at $1.10. Notice, however, that it costs only one-eleventh of that price to manufacture each pill.

Some people are willing to spend far more than $1.10, while others would only buy it if it were sold at a lower price. Foreign countries, including Canada, use government to demand a lower price, regardless of their citizens' demand for the product.

This is how price discrimination works, and how some countries use the coercive power of the state, i.e., price controls, to make sure that they secure a rock-bottom price.

As a second illustration, suppose Clear Skin targets two different groups of customers. The first group has a strong desire for Clear Skin's product and will pay $2 a pill for it. A second group is composed of Canadians. The company can sell to Canadians if it charges 20 cents a pill. Since the company is now appealing to a broader range of customers, it will sell more pills than before.

Now suppose the two groups (one made up of $2 purchasers, the other made up of 20 cent purchasers) each buy 70 million pills.

The total revenue collected will be $154 million, or $44 million more than before. The extra cost of producing the additional 40 million pills is only $4 million, so the company has increased its profit by $40 million.

Clear Skin must earn revenue to cover both its fixed and marginal costs. But it makes sense to sell the pills as long as they are priced higher than the marginal cost of production. The people who pay $2 per pill are contributing $1.90 toward recouping the fixed costs of research and development, while the customers who pay 20 cents are contributing only 10 cents to fixed costs. Still, this is better than nothing. Assuming they wouldn't purchase the pill at a higher price or their government negotiates the price, they are, nevertheless, paying something towards the research costs—which benefits everyone.

This example illustrates something else. If the US government decided this pricing structure was unfair and mandated that everyone pay 20 cents, the company would soon be out of business. Even if it sold 200 million pills at that price, it would be unable to fully pay back its investors.

In practical terms, the industry's economics dictate that as long as the large US market remains relatively free, companies will willingly sell products at below average cost—but above marginal cost—to people in other (often poor) countries. In the US domestic market, firms will develop programs that also allow them to sell at deep discounts to people who have neither drug coverage nor the income to pay full price.

Drug companies can tolerate price controls in developed countries like Canada as long as the prices cover marginal costs, and the country represents a small share of the market. But drug companies are ultimately creatures of the financial markets. They cannot raise risk capital to keep their products flowing through the pharmaceutical "pipeline" if too many customers pay prices below their sunk costs.

Firms can succeed at charging different prices to different people only if they are allowed to segment their markets. That is why

Just as movie theaters charge "matinee" prices favored by the retired, so, too, many major pharmaceutical firms offer discount cards to low-income seniors who earn too much to be covered by Medicaid, but not enough to afford an expensive Medigap policy.ᵃ Pfizer, for example, offers the Share Card, which entitles holders to 30 days worth of any Pfizer prescription for $15. To be eligible, seniors must earn less than $18,000 for individuals, $24,000 for couples, and have no other prescription coverage.ᵇ

Sources: ᵃ"Pharmaceutical Companies Step Up Promotion of Drug Discount Cards," Reuters Health, August 2, 2002.
ᵇSee "The Pfizer for Living Share Card Fact Program Sheet" at www.warner-lambert.com/pfizerinc/about/sharecard/factsheet.html.

Pfizer doesn't offer its card to all seniors—only those who need a price break and have no other option for subsidized pharmaceticals. Also, other companies, such as Lilly and GlaxoSmith-Kline, are providing discount cards for low-income seniors.

Unfortunately for pharmaceutical customers, both marketplace technology and government policy are diminishing the industry's ability to customize pricing. This point seems lost on leaders like Democrat Senator Byron Dorgan from North Dakota, a sponsor of a re-importation drug bill, who declared that his handiwork will "force pharmaceutical companies to re-price prescription drugs in this country."[178]

The likeliest outcome won't be to anyone's benefit. Companies will be forced to limit or cut off sales to the Canadian market. Pfizer, Lilly, and AstraZenica are already limiting sales to Canada to historic levels. Canadian distributors, given the opportunity to profit by sending pills to the United States, will have to decide whether to sell in Canada at lower prices, or serve the US market. If they do the former, they'll be forgoing a profitable opportunity. If they opt for the latter, the result will be shortages of drugs in Canada.

A study by the consulting firm PricewaterhouseCoopers found that prescription drugs, medical devices, and medical advances accounted for only 22 percent of the increase in premiums for 2002, a calculation that didn't account for the reduction in other health care costs that usually accompanies these advances. A larger percent of the increase, 27 percent, was driven by government mandates and regulation, lawsuits, and other risk management expenses, and fraud and abuse.
Source: "The Factors Fueling Rising Health care Costs," Prepared for the American Association of Health Plans, PricewaterhouseCoopers, April 2002.

As we've seen, there's already no such thing as a free lunch. And if Senator Dorgan and his allies in Congress get their way, there will soon be no such thing as a discounted pill.

Another threat to the health of the pharmaceutical industry is the dense and diverse mesh of rules, mandates, and voluntary contracts in which it must operate. Despite the enormous benefits the pharmaceutical industry has provided, by the turn of the century it had become the health care whipping boy. It is now under attack from the media, trial lawyers, and politicians at the federal and state levels.

CHAPTER NINETEEN:
What Role Do Lawsuits Play in Increasing Health Care Costs?

Often there are things completely outside of the medical system's control that drive up costs. The US tort system—the legal process by which victims of institutional and individual negligence sue to recover damages—is a prime example of a problem that needs addressing.

The US tort system in general is an expensive disaster. There's something wrong when a person can sue over spilt McDonald's coffee and be awarded $2.9 million because it was hot. Someone has to pay for these generous awards, and the someone is US consumers who foot the bill in small increments each time they purchase a product or service. Excessive litigation costs consumers two percent of the US economy. This translates into an annual "litigation tax" at $809 per US citizen.[179]

As bad as it is in the general economy, in health care medical malpractice suits are causing an acute crisis. Medical malpractice costs have increased at 11.9 percent a year, compounded, since 1975, or 25 times, according to a recent study.[180] In 2002, malpractice costs totaled $25 billion, or $250 per US household.

That's more than half of what the average household spent on prescription drugs.[181] And it's getting worse. The average award increased from $700,000 in 1999 to $1 million in 2001. The largest award for that year was $131 million.[182]

These awards have pushed the private medical malpractice insurance system to the brink of collapse. In 2002, insurers paid out

$1.40 for every dollar in premiums they collected. Logic dictates that this can't continue, and it hasn't. Short of reducing awards—which are actually increasing unabated—the only choice is for insurers to increase premiums or leave the market. They're doing both.

In 2002, the St. Paul Companies, which accounted for one in 10 malpractice policies in the US, left the market, citing losses. In September 2003, Farmers, the fifth largest carrier, quit writing new coverage as well. It lost $100 million in 2003. The carriers that remain in the market, including non-profit physician cooperatives, are increasing rates just to survive. According to the Congressional Budget Office (CBO), average premiums nationwide jumped 15 percent from 2000 to 2002, double the rate of medical spending.[183]

But in a country as large and diverse as the United States, averages often obscure real problem areas. That's the case here, where problems persist in both medical specialties and certain regions. The dominant carrier in Florida, for example, jacked up rates by 75 percent in Dade County from 1999 to 2002. Over the same period, the market leader in Minnesota increased rates by only two percent. The difference was more than $160,000 for the same coverage.[184] Premiums for obstetricians/gynecologists increased 22 percent nationally, and as much as 165 percent in some markets.[185]

"In some states," reports a study by the National Governor's Association, "obstetricians have stopped accepting new pregnant patients or will no longer deliver babies, and neurosurgeons will no longer staff trauma centers or emergency rooms, forcing those facilities to close or lose their rating."[186]

That's what happened in Las Vegas in 2002, when the University of Nevada Medical Center closed its trauma center for 10 days after the malpractice insurance on its surgeons jumped from $40,000 to $200,000. It resumed operation only after some of the surgeons signed up as government employees and were therefore no longer responsible for purchasing their own malpractice insurance.[187]

The American Medical Association cites 19 states that face a serious crisis due to skyrocketing premiums and the lack of carriers even willing to write high-risk but common specialties. For instance, in two West Virginia counties, only two OB units exist because of the insurance rates obstetricians were forced to pay.[188]

Residents of Mississippi have been particularly affected. One woman was forced to drive 100 miles to Tennessee to get care three weeks prior to her due date after her doctors quit practicing medicine. In fact, most communities in that state with populations under 20,000 are without doctors who deliver babies. Many have relocated to Louisiana where insurance rates are more reasonable.[189]

Institutions, too, are suffering. The American Hospital Association reports that many of its members faced a doubling of premiums from 2000 to 2001.[190] These costs, while masked, are not ultimately borne by the hospitals or doctors, but by those who pay for health care services.

A study by the Department of Health and Human Services (HHS) states that placing reasonable limits on malpractice awards would save the federal government—and hence taxpayers—$25 to $44 billion a year. HHS figures the right policy changes could reduce total health care costs by up to nine percent. This would translate into total savings of $60 to $108 billion and could make health insurance affordable for up to 4.3 million more Americans.[191]

What can be done?

To sensibly address the malpractice crisis, Americans must recognize that mistakes happen in medicine, and rarely are they caused by malevolence. It's certainly important that individuals who are harmed are compensated for the damages they suffer, or made whole with compensatory damages in legal terms. But punitive damages—those that are merely designed to punish wrongdoers and increase legal awards to lottery-like proportions—must be reigned in.

Trial lawyers, who are generally paid with a hefty cut of the huge awards rather than on flat fees, oppose such reforms and are a powerful lobby at both the state and federal levels. Still, there's been progress. California capped non-economic damages at $250,000 in 1975 with the Medical Injury Compensation Reform Act (MICRA), a law that still provides a template for other states.

The law has six other features in addition to the damage cap. It requires that juries be informed if patients have access to other sources of money for their injuries. Awards greater than $50,000 can be paid in periodic payments, rather than as a lump sum. Medical agreements can include binding arbitration clauses, which keep many disputes out of the courts. Cases must be filed within three years of an injury. Defendants must be given 90 days notice before a case is filed. In addition, the law provides a scale for reasonable attorney fees.

California's law has proven effective in keeping some control over both insurance premiums and awards. From 1997 to 2002, California's median award was $402,500. This compares to $1 million in New York and more than $800,000 in Florida and Pennsylvania.[192] Both the states' doctors and residents benefited. Malpractice insurance premiums have increased at one third the rate of the national average. The American Medical Association estimates that this saves Californians $1 billion a year in health care costs.

Twenty-six states have passed legislation that limits non-economic compensation. It's no surprise that it works. In states with caps on non-economic damages, premium increases were roughly one third of those in states with no limits on what the lawyers can collect. This reform needs to go nationwide.

The House has twice passed malpractice reform legislation, most recently in May 2004. The bill incorporates state-of-the-art reforms, the reforms that we know work to control premiums at the state level. It caps punitive damages at $250,000, institutes a three year statute of limitations, allows the courts to limit the percentage of awards that drop into the lawyers' pockets, and allows for periodic payment of awards, among other reforms.[193]

The CBO estimates that this bill could reduce premiums nationwide by an average of 25 to 30 percent.[194] In 2003, the effort died in the Senate under intense pressure from the trial lawyer lobby, the largest contributor to the Democratic Party. One hopes that the greater good will trump narrow interests soon.

CHAPTER TWENTY:
What Does the Future Hold for Quality in US Health Care?

Harvard business professor Regina Herzlinger notes in her 1997 book, *Market Driven Health Care*, that health care is the largest service industry in the US. Yet, unlike other sectors of the service economy, health care providers often lack the customer-service ethic and customized attention that has revolutionized the service economy. There are signs this is changing.

"The market forces that have reshaped much of the American economy are now working on our health care system," writes Herzlinger. "When they have completed their labors, the system will have lost its fat—inconvenience, lack of information, and high costs—but will have kept much of its muscle. A new market driven health care system will emerge."[195]

Herzlinger, who published *Consumer-Driven Health Care: Implications for Providers, Payers, and Policy Makers* in 2004, offers a satisfying answer. But is it true?

To be sure, niches in the health care economy—eye doctors, laser specialists, and cosmetic surgeons, for example—embrace the practices that characterize other successful segments of the service economy: convenient hours, posted prices, and aggressive marketing. It's no coincidence that these segments of the health care sector that do the most to meet customer needs are those where the customer pays the bill.

Over the next few decades, it is likely some health care providers will innovate and provide personalized services. Driving this revolution will be patients who will start to see themselves not as victims, but as active health care consumers.

At the dawn of the era of mass production, Henry Ford could quip that customers could choose to buy a Model T in any color they wanted, so long as it was black. Not any more. One-size-fits-all has given way to small production runs and customized ordering, from cars to computers.

Info-proficient patients

Armed with the tools of the information revolution, Americans will have the means to take more of their health care decisions into their own hands.

Already, 110 million American adults surf the web for health care information, according to a Harris poll conducted in March 2002. That's up from 97 million in the previous year's poll. Only 26 percent of Americans over age 65 have searched for health information online, but it's 49 percent for those aged 50 to 64, and 63 percent for those aged 40 to 49.[196] This suggests that much larger percentages of seniors will be looking for health information online in the future.

For physicians, the information age is another source of stress. "My blood pressure's up and my mind is spinning," writes Dr. Robert Secor. "Instead of me running the practice, the practice is running me." Why Dr. Secor's lament? In part, he says, because visits with chronic-illness patients can drag on because, "the patient will often have questions about the illness, medications, and treatment plan."[197]

Physicians will have to get used to this, just as car dealers have to accept that customers are increasingly showing up in their showrooms with detailed information on what dealers paid for the car. As the information revolution progresses, people will have even more detailed information about illnesses and their own genetic profiles.

Alternative demands

Reliance on alternative medicine is another change that is moving in the direction of consumers—though some of it may be of suspect medical value.

After sinus surgery left her with a chronic, burning facial pain, Elizabeth Calder spent a year going from physician to physician without finding relief. "I had been through the mill," she explained. "I had been to doctors who told me that the asymmetry in my face was normal. I had been to neurologists who had given me stuff for nerve pain. All the doctors looked at certain symptoms from their area of expertise." Calder finally found relief through acupuncture treatments, though she still uses conventional doctors for most health problems.[198] She is far from alone.

Studies show that five out of 10 baby boomers, and seven out of 10 post-boomers, use some form of alternative health care, which has started gaining significant support from the US government. In 1998, the National Institutes of Health elevated the Office of Alternative Medicine to the National Center for Complementary and Alternative Medicine. Funding for the center rose from $2 million in 1993 to $100.6 million in fiscal 2002.[199]

Regardless of the value of many alternative therapies, this is one more sign that customers can drive markets.

Consumer-driven health plans

US employers want to engender the employee goodwill that comes with offering medical insurance, but they also want to put an end to the relentless price increases. There is, fortunately, a constructive way to go.

In the future, many companies will harness market forces through what are known as "consumer-driven" health plans. This umbrella term covers a variety of approaches, such as the cafeteria plans of large employers and defined-contribution health plans.[200]

The idea is to provide employees with flexibility and choice and, at the same time, allow companies to limit the total amount they spend on health care. "Increasingly, employers are looking at their pension benefits as a model," writes Galen Institute policy analyst Greg Scandlen. "They have successfully moved their retirement programs from defined benefits to Defined Contribution programs like 401(k)s. Employees are happy to control their investments and shape their own futures. Employers are happy to have a fixed, budgetable obligation administered by professional money managers."[201]

Yale University offers its employees a variety of health care plans, from the Yale Health Plan, a staff model HMO that relies on a local health center and the Yale–New Haven hospital, to Blue Cross HMO and more flexible point-of-service plans. Employees are free to choose a plan that suits their individual needs. If they choose the Yale Health Plan, the individual and family premiums are set at $0 for faculty who earn less than $70,000 a year. If individuals choose the other options, they'll pay more.
(Source: http://www.yale.edu/ hronline/benefits/01fa.html.)

While only a few pure defined-contribution plans have emerged, many companies and organizations already practice a version of defined-contribution health plans.

Defined-contribution arrangements

The Federal Employees Health Benefits Program (FEHBP), as well as many large corporations, harnesses consumer choice to keep prices down. This works even if the employer's low-cost option isn't an in-house product. The FEHBP arrangement, in essence, is a version of defined-contribution health insurance. It provides employees an incentive to choose the low-cost option—and thus keep total costs down—while it doesn't prevent them from paying for an option that better suits them.

According to a recent survey by the Kaiser Family Foundation, among firms that offer a choice of more than one health plan, 17 percent of those firms use a defined contribution arrangement.

Small firms (those with fewer than 200 employees) are much less likely to offer a choice of plans. Interestingly, those that do offer a choice are more likely to use a defined contribution plan (28 percent) than are the larger firms—a sure sign of the cost advantages of such plans.[202]

HRAs and HSAs

Other emerging health care products are Health Reimbursement Arrangements (HRAs) and Health Savings Accounts (HSAs). HRAs are used in the employer group market. HSAs, created by the 2003 Medicare bill, are available to individuals.

The concepts driving these products are simple and time tested. People spend their own money more wisely than someone else's. This insight is wedded to the empirical fact that most people spend very little money each year on health care. What they need is insurance against large expenses.

Therefore, these products combine a tax-advantaged savings account with a high-deductible insurance policy. Individuals can pay routine expenses from the savings account. Any money left over can either remain in the account for future expenses or, under some circumstances, be withdrawn and spent. This returns insurance to its proper function and reduces administrative expenses for small claims.

Companies such as Definity Health, based in St. Louis Park, Minnesota; Destiny Health, based in Bethesda, Maryland; Lumenos, based in Alexandria, Virginia; Golden Rule Insurance, based in Indianapolis, Indiana; and even some large commercial insurers are offering innovative consumer-driven products that, while protecting individuals against major medical expenses, make them conscious shoppers for health services.

MSAs

Medical Savings Accounts (MSAs) were created as a pilot program in 1996. Set up to fail, the accounts were restricted to small businesses and the self-employed, and the government dictated the details of the benefit plans. MSAs are treated by policymakers as a public policy experiment, and so are quite limited in the number of enrollees. The legislation that created MSAs has proven to be too narrow in scope to have a big impact on health benefits.

Consumer-driven future

In all of these myriad forms, a switch to consumer-driven policies will reduce costs, which in turn will allow health care providers to offer greater quality. The consumer revolution in health will not only bring benefits to patients. It will benefit employers as well.

"Employers want to stop being 'the monkey in the middle,'" writes Scandlen, who notes that employers often get very little

---

Thirty-three-year-old Cheryl Brock, a benefit analyst for Humana, signed up for an HRA plan in 2001 after considering all her options (including standard HMO and PPO plans). In exchange for taking a manageable financial risk, she reduced her share of the monthly premium to just over $10, a 75-percent drop. Here's how her plan works. Her employer pays her first $500 in annual medical expenses.

Brock is then responsible for the entire tab until she's spent $2,000, or incurred $2,500 in total expenses. At that point, her insurance takes over 100 percent of all expenses.

She saves $390 annually by reducing her share of the premium, so she comes out ahead unless she spends more than $890 for care. "I think it's well worth the risk," she told USA Today. It'll definitely make her a better shopper. "Depending on what the doctor wanted to test me for and why, I would determine whether I wanted to do that. It's my responsibility to evaluate the cost of care."

(Source: Julie Appleby, "New Insurance Plans Turn Patients into Shoppers, Some Consumers Willing to Gamble They'll Stay Well," USA Today, January 8, 2002.)

---

thanks for spending up to $6,000 a year per employee, and are weary of reams of government regulations. "They want to get out of managing health benefits. At the same time, they want their workforce covered and productive."[203]

Defined contribution plans, HRAs, and HSAs are just a sign of the plethora of consumer-friendly, cost-controlling, quality-boosting programs that could be around the corner. In order for these programs to be viable, however, the United States will have to move from a system of employer-provided health care to refundable tax credits attached to individuals. Only in this way can plans be developed that are tailored to individual needs (and, in most cases, have some degree of portability).

With such credits, workers could switch jobs without having health insurance as a factor in their decision. Like a pure defined contribution, these credits provide people with money they can use to purchase their own health-insurance policy. Refundable tax credits make health care financing fairer and more transparent.

As of January 2002, an estimated 350,000 Americans were enrolled in consumer-driven health plans. They are attractive to large and small business alike. One in five employers says it would like to offer such a plan, and many large employers are starting to do so, including Medtronic, Raytheon, and the University of Minnesota.[204]

CHAPTER TWENTY-ONE:
How would Consumer-driven Health Care Affect Doctors? How could it Benefit the Uninsured, Seniors, and All Consumers?

As we've seen, consumer-driven plans have inherent strengths. But are they flexible enough for the poor, the uninsured, and the elderly?

Remember, consumer-driven health plans make use of either Medical Savings Accounts (MSAs) or Health Savings Accounts (HSAs) tied to individuals, or Health Reimbursement Arrangements (HRAs) tied to individuals and their employment.

Both forms provide funds to individuals and families to spend on medical goods and services below a high deductible. With consumer-driven plans, individuals spend money toward the actual prices of drugs. This enables consumers, with the help of their physicians, to weigh the benefits and costs of competing drugs.

If a low-cost generic drug works fine for a patient, he can pay less and retain the savings in his MSA, HSA, or HRA for future needs. If, however, a higher-priced drug works better, the patient also gains because the drug may keep him from entering the hospital or incurring other medical expenses that would cost even more.

The main restriction is that HRAs must be funded by employers, not by employee salary deductions. Other than that, HRAs are very flexible. They can be set up by any business, large or small. They can be funded at any amount. They can even be set up without being tied to a specific insurance plan or without any insurance plan at all.

Benefits for consumers and doctors alike

HRAs, HSAs, and other consumer-driven health plans are just the beginning of a movement to put in place a real marketplace for health care. Consumers will be faced with the real prices of the non-catastrophic medical goods and services they consume, but with the advantage of having greater flexibility and choice. Insurance, in turn, will be limited to unpredictable, high-expense medical events that seldom occur—in just the way most other types of insurance operate.

Several start-up companies have been formed—with names such as Definity Health, Lumenos, and Destiny Health—to administer these new, consumer-driven health plans. They focus on providing information to employees through the use of web sites, enabling employees to act as informed consumers. HRAs, however, can be set up by employers without the help of these companies.

A consumer-driven market for health care will also benefit doctors and other providers of health care. These professionals have seen their salaries reduced under pressure from governments and managed care. In a real marketplace, doctors could price their services much more freely.

This is essential to making medicine a profession that young people will want to go into.

The typical medical school graduate incurs debt in the six-figure range. If there are no opportunities to make a good salary, the next generation will conclude that becoming a doctor is a poor investment. If governments dictate to doctors how health care must be performed, young people will find a better use for their talents.

HSAs for the uninsured

Tax credits and vouchers would give a direct government subsidy to individuals and families to purchase health-insurance policies unconnected to the workplace. By giving people direct control over the insurance policy they purchase, the tax credit/voucher would also promote the sale of catastrophic health insurance combined with Health Savings Accounts.

There is a savings to be had here, one that allows us to improve the lot of seniors and the unemployed. Recall the District of Columbia insurance commissioner's explanation about the inherent contradiction at the core of most managed-care plans? Insurance, he noted, works best when it's used infrequently. That's why life, homeowners, and automobile insurance are all affordable—because we don't want to die, and we can't use car insurance to change the oil and fill up our gas tanks. Health insurance should work along the same lines.

Ordinary health maintenance should not be treated as an event that triggers insurance coverage. Health maintenance should be encouraged—catch problems early and they are treated with more ease and at less expense—but not by making insurance a ubiquitous form of financing. Managed care seeks to promote health maintenance through the use of low co-payments, but this has promoted the idea that individuals are entitled to subsidized payments for all types of health care.

HSAs provide a better answer for consumers of all conditions, ages, and levels of income.

Originally developed in the 1970s by Jesse Hixson, an economist at the American Medical Association, the concept of MSAs and HSAs were popularized by health economists John Goodman and Gerald Musgrave in their 1992 book, *Patient Power*. They were introduced in the real world by health insurance pioneer J. Patrick Rooney's Golden Rule Insurance Company and the Virginia-based utility Dominion Resources.[205]

As we've seen, HSA plans combine a high deductible insurance policy with a tax-free savings account dedicated to paying for expenses below the insurance deductible. Any unused funds at the end of the year are rolled over and remain tax-free, as long as they are not withdrawn to purchase non-health care items.

HSAs address some of the key problems affecting health care in the United States. They control health care costs by making people price sensitive. This is done by separating out routine and maintenance health spending from the insurance function. HSAs also address a critical imbalance in health care spending. In 1996, 10 percent of Americans accounted for 69 percent of health expenditures. Some 30 percent of Americans accounted for 90 percent of expenditures.[206]

The flip side of this fact is good news—a large majority of Americans do not spend much on health care. Most Americans, however, have insurance or managed-care coverage that pays for these small and routine expenses, and large administrative expenses for claims are incurred in the process. With HSAs, those expenses are avoided for all but the few who actually use their insurance. This alone adds up to significant savings.

But HSAs offer an even more powerful cost control arrangement. Notice that HSAs change the incentives that an individual faces. Under first-dollar managed care, a person faces a "use-it-or-lose-it" situation. The savings from any health care not consumed does not benefit the individual, but goes into a common pool.

For people who have HSAs, however, money that is not spent from the cash account in any given year is retained. It rolls over to the next year and collects interest. Over time, individuals can build up a health care nest egg. It's a product premised on savings, not spending.

HSAs also address the problem of managed care. While the insurance product will in many cases be a managed network, the patient, not the insurance company, will be the one deciding which doctor to see. Once in the doctor's office, there won't be a third party to intrude on the doctor/patient relationship. Doctors often offer deep discounts for those who are willing to pay in full by cash or check at the time of the visit.

SimpleCare, for instance, was started in Washington State but has been rapidly expanding into other states. Under SimpleCare, doctors charge a simple, three-tiered payment scale corresponding to "Short," "Medium," and "Long" visits. (Dr. Vern Cherewatenko reports that he charges $35 for a "Short" visit and nets $5, while under managed care, he received a $79 payment for the same visit but lost $7 because administrative expenses were so much greater.[207])

Furthermore, HSAs are no longer an untested theory, thanks to the MSA pilot program. They are at work in the real world. The Cato Institute in Washington, DC, has employed an MSA with catastrophic insurance since 1997 when they first received favorable tax treatment. From 1997 through 2000, Cato's insurance premiums have remained constant. The average unused funds retained in MSAs were $1,143 per year for individual employees and $1,181 per year for employees with family coverage.[208]

The cutting-edge health food grocery chain Whole Foods switched to a HRA/MSA-style health plan in 2003. The company offers high deductible insurance to its employees—$500 for prescriptions and $1,000 for standard medical care. It also deposits from $300 to $1,800 each year in a health savings account. The results have been outstanding. Employee coverage has increased from 65 percent to 95 percent, as employees no longer face a premium. Medical claims dropped 13 percent while hospital admissions plummeted by 22 percent. The company's costs held constant in a year when similar employers with traditional plans faced increases of 14 percent. The best part: only one in 10 employees drained their savings account. This meant that $14 million—$560 per account—rolled over for medical use in 2004 or future years.[209]

Even without tax benefits, MSAs have proven to work well. Golden Rule Insurance Company is a large employer that doesn't qualify for tax-free MSAs, which allow the tax-free rollover of unspent account balances from one year to the next. Nevertheless, it has offered two MSA plans to its employees for several years. Since the MSAs are not free from taxes, Golden Rule employees often withdraw their unspent balances at the end of the year. In 2000, 79 percent of their employees withdrew unspent MSA balances averaging $989.[210]

Congress: Why MSAs were lagging

While MSAs were popular with employees, they haven't been popular with most Democrats in Congress. In 1996, advocates for MSAs were finally able to get Congress to pass a pilot MSA program as part of the Health Insurance Portability and Accountability Act (HIPAA) of 1996. Although ostensibly a move to free up health insurance, Congress tightly regulated the plans and doomed them to being a small market niche.

First, the law limits the total number of people who can open accounts to 750,000—a pittance given the health insurance market under age 65. This restriction limited the profits companies could expect to earn from developing products for this market. Not that there was much of a market or many product options to develop. Congress also limited the market to self-employed persons and companies with fewer than 50 employees.[211] This shut out companies most able to develop MSAs in-house—those with professional human resource departments.

Congress also designed the insurance product, setting initial deductibles between $1,500 and $2,250 for individual coverage and between $3,000 and $4,500 for family coverage. Those limits were indexed for inflation and in 2003 were raised to $1,700 to $2,500 for individuals and $3,350 to $5,050 for families.[212] The maximum annual contribution to the MSA was set at 65 percent of the deductible for individual policies and 75 percent of the deductible for family policies.[213]

This tight range meant that the products were uneconomical for many companies. Not surprisingly, few purchased the product, with only about 42,000 policies in existence in 1998.[214] On a successful note, nearly 40 percent of those who purchased MSA plans in 1997 were previously uninsured, showing the attractiveness of affordable health insurance.

Finally, just to underscore how little respect Congress had for the concept, the law made this MSA program temporary.

The program, a cynic might note, was designed to fail. The solution was to deregulate the program. That's what Congress did when it created HSAs in 2003.

HSAs for seniors

HSAs represent a good solution for the employed. What about seniors?

As we've seen, Medicare is increasingly a program that abuses physicians even as it provides incomplete coverage for US seniors. Despite these drawbacks, its costs continue upward at an unsupportable pace.

Medicare needs an incremental approach that puts to work the combined power of individual consumer choice and the market. Scholars at the Heritage Foundation have spent years studying Medicare and developing ideas for reform. Interestingly, the approach they propose is exactly the approach the federal government takes for its own employees.

Instead of developing 110,000 pages of regulations and harassing doctors in the service of cost control, it would be better to provide seniors with vouchers for health insurance. Seniors could use these vouchers to purchase private insurance from plans that were pre-approved by the federal government. Everyone would be entitled to care that is at least as generous as the package offered by Medicare today. But many would choose to purchase plans that provided extra services, such as prescription drugs or eye care. Some might purchase an HSA package. Others might elect to purchase a managed-care package that promises generous coverage in exchange for a limited selection of physicians. Some seniors might elect to pay extra for comprehensive benefits and unfettered choice. Plans would compete for seniors' business, and in so doing there would be intense pressure to provide as many services as possible for the lowest possible price.

This same voucher approach, which relies on the power of consumer choice, should be applied to Medicaid, the federal/state health program for low-income Americans.

CHAPTER TWENTY-TWO:
Innovation is Alive and Well

The United States is mired in a quasi-socialist medical system that distorts incentives to provide good health care, while degrading the doctor-patient relationship. In reaction, doctors and patients alike are seeking out ways to get around the system—and even outside of it, altogether.

The wider promise of boutique or "concierge" practices

As we've seen, many physicians are deeply frustrated with the demands managed care organizations have made of them. While managed care was able to reduce costs in the 1990s, there are many patients and doctors who are dissatisfied with it.[215] Combined with the increasing bureaucratization of Medicare and its declining payments, some doctors are concluding that enough is enough, quitting practices dependent on managed care, and starting "concierge" or "boutique" practices.

In exchange for an annual fee ranging from $1,500 to $20,000 per family, these practices offer personalized services, such as 24-hour phone contact with the physicians, and luxury amenities, such as personalized robes and a well-appointed doctor's office. The fees cover services that are not covered by Medicare or traditional insurance. Patients, therefore, rely on their insurance to cover additional medical expenses.

The extra time these emerging practices spend on patients can be quite extensive. MD2, a boutique practice in Seattle with plans to expand to New York, Los Angeles, and other major cities, charges $20,000 a year for a couple to join the practice that was founded by Dr. Howard Maron, the former doctor of the Seattle Super-Sonics. For this fee, patients get a 50-to-1 patient-to-doctor ratio—compared to a ratio as high as 4,000-to-1 in some practices. And they get constant care, regardless of when or where they need it.

Dr. Maron, for example, arranged care via cell phone for a patient whose hip replacement failed while on a trip to Hong Kong. "We thought, 'Oh gee, that's quite a bit of money,'" 65-year-old David Heerensperger, the distressed Hong Kong traveler, told the *New York Times*. "Even if it was half again as much, it's still nice to have that service available."[216]

Heerensperger's view is not universal, especially among academics who work in health policy. The emergence of concierge practices came to a head when Dr. Steven R. Flier and Dr. Jordan S. Busch, internists at Boston's Beth Israel Deaconess Medical Center, decided to give up their 4,200-person practice for a boutique practice of just 300 people. They see two or three patients a day, as opposed to 24 under their old practice. Their entrepreneurial move was treated as a defection by the local press, academic commentators, and their former colleagues.[217]

Dr. John D. Goodson, a professor at Harvard Medical School and a primary-care physician, blasts the concierge practices. "The implication that well-heeled patients have the right to something more is abhorrent," he told the *Boston Globe*.[218] Tufts Health Plan, a Boston-area HMO, asked state officials to determine whether the doctors' new practice complies with insurance laws.[219]

"It just doesn't sit right," Nancy Achin Sullivan, executive director of the Massachusetts Board of Registration in Medicine, told the *New York Times*. She investigated the practice and found nothing illegal. Still, she's open to the suggestion that it ought not to be allowed. "Is this the type of practice and the type of medicine that the board members would like to see in Massachusetts?" she asks. "The answer is clearly no."[220]

Even the feds have gotten into the act. On March 4, 2002, five Democratic congressmen led by Henry Waxman sent a letter to

Health and Human Services (HHS) Secretary Tommy Thompson asking him to "stop the spread of premium medical services." The practices were "raising concerns of access and affordability in the Medicare program." Waxman also told reporters that an annual fee "violates limits on charges for services" and violates the False Claims Act by "understating true charges." HHS said it had no plans to issue a ruling in the near future.[221]

Senator Bill Nelson, a Florida Democrat who represents many Medicare beneficiaries, has introduced a bill that would prevent concierge practices from charging Medicare patients an annual fee. The result of such a law is easy to predict. It would make the practices more exclusive, not less. Such practices would exist for retirees who are wealthy enough to reach into their pockets for the annual fee, and also pay out-of-pocket for each office visit.

These criticisms ignore the beneficial—and even egalitarian—promise of these practices. Wealthy Americans, and their counterparts around the world, have always been able to cut personal deals with doctors. They've always received more personalized care.

This is true for the mega-rich, who can afford to retain doctors for their exclusive use. It's true for athletes, who have 24-hour-a-day, 7-day-a-week access to team specialists. It's true for corporate executives, who have access to red-carpet treatment from such clinics as Cleveland's Center for Corporate Health, all paid for by the company.[222] What the emerging concierge practices offer is a proliferation of the model to the upper-middle-class.

Sure, MD2, which considers itself to be the Ritz-Carlton of concierge practices, charges $20,000. But others charge as little as $1,500, a sum that is within reach for upper middle-class families that want to purchase more personalized care. The true significance of the concierge practice is that it's democratizing luxury.

Two packs a day

When one patient scolded Dr. Flier for abandoning him for the wealthy, Dr. Flier pointed out that, at two packs of cigarettes a day, the patient's smoking habit costs him more than the fee for personalized care. "No one goes around saying that smoking is a habit only for the wealthy," says Dr. Flier. "People do make choices within a range of dollars."[223]

Doctors such as Flier and Busch are entrepreneurs. The managed-care revolution, which increased their patient load from 2,500 patients per doctor to 4,200 patients per doctor, led them to believe they could find a better way to add value.[224] In so doing, they expect to be able to offer better care, make more money, and have more time to perform volunteer work.

Critics of concierge medicine say that lower-income people will be left behind. They fail to understand how the market economy produces innovations that become available to everyone. New products and technology, often expensive, are initially consumed only by the wealthy who have the disposable income to spend on expensive new items. This revenue allows companies to develop efficient production processes and reduce unit costs. When these changes happen in medical care, there should be no more criticism than when they happen for automobiles, computers, or even financial services.

Generally, the rich purchase Lexuses, the middle-class buy Toyota Camrys, the lower middle-class buy Toyota Echos. Antilock brakes, which were initially available only on luxury cars, are now an available option on all automobiles. Inequality isn't what's remarkable. What's remarkable is how quickly innovations that were once available only to the rich become commonplace when the market is left free to operate. As Nobel laureate in economics Milton Friedman says, "the rich work for the poor." [225]

E-consultations

Drs. Chuck Kilo and Steve Gordon are engaged in another experiment on the West Coast to give their patients more personalized care. Their patients pay $350 a year, which buys them e-mail access to the physicians as well as a place in their practice. The physicians don't take insurance co-payments. The money isn't worth the paperwork. "You've got a lot of baby boomers and gen-X-ers who are used to a very high level of service in the rest of their lives," Dr. Kilo told *US News & World Report*. "We want to take health care to a different level."[226]

Many doctors aren't using e-mail because they aren't reimbursed for the time. The fee takes care of that. It may seem impersonal, but it is far more cost-effective than the telephone, which requires the doctor and patient to be free simultaneously. Often issues can be dealt with online which obviates the need for an office visit. That, in turn, frees up the schedule for sicker patients who require more time. "The huge advantage is having access to the doctor," says 39-year-old Blake Patsy. "For the average Joe who's hesitant about the doctor's office, there's a huge value."[227]

Personalization

More people are demanding personalized health care and showing a willingness to reach into their pockets to pay for it. Many are confounding the medical establishment by insisting on getting what they want when they want it. The explosive growth of the for-profit body scan industry proves that Americans aren't willing to be led around and told "no" by managed care.

The same forces producing concierge practices—physician and patient disaffection with the constraints of managed care combined with rising affluence—are producing another popular service: Stand-alone diagnostic body scans. While concierge practices make available to the upper-middle-class what was once the sole province of the super-rich, a burgeoning for-profit body scan industry is also putting within reach of the middle-class what was once only available for the wealthy.

CT scans are powerfully effective x-rays that can detect a variety of health problems from weak spots in arteries, to small tumors, to the conditions that cause heart disease. In the United States, ever since such powerful imaging devices as MRIs (Magnetic Resonance Imaging scanners) and CT scanners became available, wealthy people have been able to purchase expensive scans as part of their annual check-ups. Today, these diagnostic tools are within the reach of ordinary Americans, thanks to decreasing costs of technology and entrepreneurial companies.

CAT Scan 2000, a self-described Wal-Mart of scanning, operates six tractor-trailer scanning units. Based in Florida, each of the company's units are staffed with a technician who runs the machine and an administrator who handles the cash payments. They usually set up shop in the parking lot of a local church, whose pastor receives free scans for himself and his family for extending the courtesy. Customers can choose to have one region of their body scanned for $199 or their entire body for $567.[228]

Radiologists in Florida read the images and mail reports to customers, who receive them in a matter of weeks. The scans often detect problems that otherwise would go untreated. Doctors at the Cooper Clinic, a Dallas-based scan company, have found solid kidney tumors in 70 individuals. All but three were cancerous.[229]

It's no wonder that ex-smokers, such as 47-year-old nurse Tanya Ingle, jumped at the chance to get her lungs scanned. Her uncle had lung cancer and she asked her doctor for a scan, to ensure she was clear. Her doctor refused to order the scan, saying there was no medical reason for it. When CAT Scan 2000 rolled into town, she happily reached into her own pocket to pay for the peace of mind.[230]

One might expect this development to be heralded, especially in the light of the massive amounts of information Americans have received on the dangers of smoking, drinking, and fatty diets. Catch problems early, Americans are often told, and they are more easily and cheaply treated. Yet experts decry the scans and gripe that they no longer control patients' decisions.

"This is a pretty heavy-duty exam that seems to have sort of escaped into the marketplace," Dr. Larry Kessler, the federal employee who directs the office of surveillance and biometrics at the Food and Drug Administration, lamented to the *New York Times*. "We have a technology that's gotten caught in the gaps between the scientific agencies, and the payers who pay for health care of all sorts. The fair evaluation of these procedures is no one's province. That's the gap here."[231]

Actually, the gap is in the thinking of bureaucrats such as Kessler. They are operating under the old mindset, one in which patients did as they were told and didn't ask questions. But today, when patients are told no, they are likely to take things into their own hands. When Ingle's doctor told her no, she thought being a statistic wasn't good enough for her. She paid for her own scan.

Critics complain that this personal spending may end up increasing costs for the insured sector of the health care system. That's because the bills for follow-up appointments to further diagnose and treat conditions identified by the scans will often be paid by insurance. This may be true, or it may prove false. If early detection makes treatment more effective and cheaper, the units could turn out to decrease costs. It's an empirical question—one for which there are insufficient data to answer.

The broader point is that free people ought to be able to spend their own money to get peace of mind, even if their doctor or managed-care company says that statistics show they have nothing to worry about. The "fair evaluation" of the medical procedures, to borrow Dr. Kessler's phrase, should ultimately rest with the patient. Thanks to companies such as CAT Scan 2000, it does. This trend toward the personalization of medicine is sure to continue.

Full-service pharmacies

Roles are changing, and no one knows this better than pharmacists. In the old days, the pharmacy was a local business, with neighborhood pharmacists dispensing drugs to patients. Chain stores first challenged this way of doing business with their ability to offer lower prices based on volume.

But with overnight delivery, large managed-care companies, and lightening fast information systems, now the chain stores are under pressure from mail-order pharmacies. The cost advantage—and effects of the evolving drug patterns—hit home in New York City in March 2002 when New York's Health and Human Service Employees Union SEIU 1199 announced that it was contracting with AdvancePCS to fill members' prescriptions for long-term conditions.

The company offered the union a 22-percent discount from listed wholesale prices, a savings that meant $5 to $6 million a year for the union, which covers 250,000 individuals.[232] Some of those 250,000 individuals happened to be working pharmacists in New York, people who were already feeling the competitive heat from mail-order competition.

"This doesn't make sense to me," Frank Strafaci, a Rite-Aid pharmacist and union member, told the *New York Times*. "I'm shocked that this program may take jobs away from union members."[233] Union officials first defended the program as necessary to keep offering generous benefits, but they backed down under pressure, making the program voluntary.

Yet even as New York's pharmacists fight to keep the city's pill supply local, pharmacists in other parts of the country are expanding into different areas to stay vital. The Kerr Drug Store in Chapel Hill, North Carolina, offers bone-density tests, smoking cessation clinics, and women's health courses, in addition to drugs.[234] In Florida, pharmacists can prescribe some routine drugs. In 32 states, they can offer flu and pneumonia shots.

"Pharmacists are accessible to people," Eleni Anagnostiadis, executive director of the National Institute for Standards in Pharmacist Credentialing, told the *New York Times*. "Patients see their pharmacists more than their doctor."[235] It's a dynamic process that serves to push prices lower, even as it puts services and products closer to patients.

Technology and consumer empowerment

Technology and the communications revolution are enabling massive changes in medicine. Not only do ordinary people have, at a mouse click away, access to in-depth information, but so, too, do physicians and other health professionals. Inexpensive communication and storage and retrieval of information are changing the health care system in many ways. The question, as always, is will government policy adapt to keep up?

Harvard Professor Michael Porter recommends the free flow of information to consumers. As he so aptly states, "Information is integral to competition in any well-functioning market. It allows buyers to shop for the best value and forces sellers to compare themselves to rivals. In health care, though, the information really needed to support value-creating competition has been largely absent or suppressed."[236]

Now, more than ever, the regulatory lines that keep various components of the health care system separate and distinct—doctor, nurse, technician, pharmacist—are increasingly seen as arbitrary.

Telemedicine

In the global economy, information travels fast and technology diffuses quickly as long as there are people willing to pay its initial cost. When new practices work best for both patients and providers, they will be widely adopted. One trend that makes sense is the use of telemedicine.

Although the medical profession, at least in the United States, has debated the appropriateness of the telephone as a tool of medicine, it's safe to say that such issues are no longer controversial.[237] Telemedicine was officially employed as early as 1964, when the first closed-circuit television link was built between the Nebraska Psychiatric Institute in Omaha and Norfolk State Hospital, a distance of over 100 miles.[238]

These days, with high-speed data networks making video communication easy and relatively inexpensive, telemedicine is used for everything from bringing big-city medicine to remote areas, to keeping terminally ill patients comfortable at home, rather than in hospice care.

This technology is at work in rural America. Over the last decade, telemedicine, which is used in 42 states, has brought medical specialists into the smallest villages. In Kansas, a state where one-third of counties have population densities so low that they still qualify as frontiers, getting timely access to medical specialists has always been challenging.

Prior to telemedicine, doctors had to be flown to remote areas, an expensive and time-consuming option that's not available on many harsh winter days. Now it means hooking up a televideo and telemonitoring technologies, often over the Internet, so that specialists can conduct full examinations, assisted on the other end by nurses and perhaps a family doctor.

"Clinicians (can) assess, manage, and treat off-site patients and exchange digital radiographs, pathological images, and multimedia medical records," writes Dr. Ace Allen, a medical oncologist and founding member of the American Telemedicine Association. "Home monitoring of EEGs, EKGs, temperature, blood pressure, and infusion pumps is also becoming possible, saving patients exhausting trips across the country in rural areas, and across the city in urban areas."[239]

Rapidly falling costs are one factor that has made telemedicine possible. Videoconferencing equipment that once cost $100,000 is now available for $12,000. Some units are as inexpensive as $3,500.[240] Telemedicine not only facilitates long-distance examinations, but it also allows for home monitoring of patients. Homebound patients get more frequent monitoring, several times a day and on demand, instead of several times a week.

The value of telemedicine hit home for hospice nurse Barbara Johnson when she arrived at the home of a 27-year-old breast cancer patient who was in severe pain. It took her four hours to get a morphine system up and running. It took care of the pain but didn't provide her with peace of mind. "I was an hour and a half away," she recalls. "If something happened to the machine, it might take hours to get the IV functioning again. The family would have to call an ambulance, and the patient might go for four or five hours without adequate pain control. I knew there had to be a better way."[241]

There was. Barbara Johnson heard about telemedicine and convinced her employer, Kaiser Permanente, to experiment with it. Now this option is available to her patients. "Immuno-compromised, malnourished, fatigued, and pain-ridden cancer patients shouldn't have to be carted around to be seen," she says. "They spend more time being taken to the clinic than seeing the practitioner after they arrive. Using home telecare for routine evaluations is so much better for everyone."

The creativity inherent in these new programs serves as living proof that in health care, as in other aspects of our lives, people can be inventive when they are allowed to be. There is no reason why health care can't be as innovative as other aspects of our economy in terms of responding to what people need and want. Free-market choice, as always, drives a healthy competition that inevitably leads to better goods and services, more convenience, more choice, and better pricing.

CHAPTER TWENTY-THREE:
Consumer Power is the Answer

After a half-century or so of experimentation, the results are clear. Too much government intervention into US health care hasn't been good—for patients, doctors, or taxpayers. Experience shows that consumer-directed programs such as HRAs, HSAs, and PBMs can go a long way toward restoring the doctor-patient relationship.

By placing decision-making back into the hands of the consumer, we can empower patients to choose their doctors and their health plans.

We can empower doctors to restore the primacy of the doctor-patient relationship.

We can reduce the upward pressure on health care costs and extend broader coverage.

And we can bring in those left out of the current insurance system.

Human ingenuity—once freed from constraint—has already begun the work of creating a new age of health services to the benefit of all. The challenge is for legislators and regulators in the United States to catch up.

Notes to Part I

Preface

1. "BC Government, Health Union Reach Settlement," *Globeandmail.com*, Monday, May 3, 2004.

Foreword

2. Aleksandr I. Solzhenitsyn, *The Cancer Ward* (New York: The Dial Press, 1968), chap. 30, "The Old Doctor," pp. 478-496; top quote, pp. 190-191.

Introduction

3. US Department of Labor: Bureau of Labor Statistics, "Consumer Expenditures in 2002 (annual report)," Table 3 and Table 7. Available at *http://www.bls.gov/cex/home.htm#tables* (accessed February 2004).

4. Centers for Medicare & Medicaid Services, "The Nation's Health Dollar: 2001." Available at *http://www.cms.hhs.gov/statistics/nhe/historical/chart.asp* (accessed July 1, 2003).

5. Larry Levitt *et al.*, "Employer Health Benefits: 2001 Annual Survey," The Henry J. Kaiser Family Foundation and Health Research and Educational Trust (September 2001).

6. See Barbara Crossette, "Canada's Health Care Shows Strains," *New York Times*, October 11, 2001.

Chapter One

7. Michael E. Porter and Elizabeth Olmstead Teisberg, "Redefining Competition in Health Care," *Harvard Business Review*, June 2004, pp. 65-76.

8. "Historical National Health Expenditures by Type of Service and Source of Funds: Calendar Years 1960-2001," Centers for Medicare and Medicaid Services. Available at *http://www.cms.hhs.gov/statistics/nhe/default.asp#download* (accessed April 11, 2003).

9. John C. Goodman and Gerald L. Musgrave, *Patient Power: Solving America's Health Care Crisis,* (Washington, DC: Cato Institute, 1992), p. 290.

10. Katherine Levit *et al.*, "Inflation Spurs Health Spending in 2000," *Health Affairs* Vol. 21 No. 1 (January/February 2002): 172–181.

11. David Dranove, *The Economic Evolution of American Health Care: From Marcus Welby to Managed Care,* (Princeton, NJ: Princeton University Press, 2000), p. 48.

12. Rhonda L. Rundle, "Oft-Derided Veterans Health Agency Puts Data Online, Saving Time, Lives," *Wall Street Journal*, December 10, 2001.

13. See special instructions on order page for Peter A. Pavarini, Esq. (ed), *United States Health Care Laws and Rules 2004-2005 Edition*, www.healthlawyers.com.

Chapter Two

14. For a persuasive articulation of this view, see Paul Starr, *The Social Transformation of American Medicine* (New York: Basic Books, 1982)

15. Starr, *The Social Transformation of American Medicine*, p. 200.

16. See "The Hill-Burton Free Care Program," US Department of Health and Human Services, Health Resources and Services Administration. Available at *http://www.hrsa.gov/osp/dfcr/about/aboutdiv.htm* (accessed June 24, 2003).

17. Roger D. Feldman, ed., *American Health Care: Government, Market Processes, and Public Interest* (Oakland, CA: The Independent Institute, 2000), pp. 243-251.

18. Dranove, *The Economic Evolution of Health Care*, p. 54.

19. Sue A. Blevins, *Medicare's Midlife Crisis* (Washington, DC: Cato Institute, 2001), p. 81.

20. Dranove, *The Economic Evolution of Health Care*, p. 57.

21. Health Maintenance Organization Act of 1973. Public Law 93-222, 93rd Congress, 1st Session, December 29, 1973.

Chapter Three

22. The Bipartisan Consensus Managed Care Improvement Act (Division B of H.R. 2990), Sec. 104(d). Quote in John S. Hoff, Esq., *The Patients' Bill of Rights: A Prescription for Massive Federal Regulation*, The Heritage Foundation Backgrounder, No. 1350 (February 29, 2000), p. 11.

23. Hoff, *The Patients' Bill of Rights*, p. 2.

Chapter Four

24. Quoted in Jennifer Steinhauer, "Health Care: The Sound and the Fury," *New York Times*, December 16, 2001.

25. George D. Lundberg with James Stacey, *Severed Trust: Why American Medicine Hasn't Been Fixed* (New York: Basic Books, 2000), p. 38.

26. In 2000, 177 million Americans had private, employer-sponsored health insurance according to the US Census.

27. *Employer Health Benefits 2001 Annual Survey, Market Share of Health Plans,* The Henry J. Kaiser Family Foundation, Section 6.

28. Dranove, *The Economic Evolution of American Health Care*, pp. 87-89.

29. "People & the Press Favorability Poll," Pew Research Center, July 24, 2001.

Chapter Five

30. Susan Milligan, "4-Year Battle Reduced to Money," *Boston Globe*, July 9, 2001.

31. "The Managed Care Evolution," *Health Affairs*, vol. 23, no. 2 (March/April 2004): 28.

32. Starr, *The Social Transformation of American Medicine*, p. 202.

33. Starr, *The Social Transformation of American Medicine*, pp. 206-209.

34. Health Maintenance Organization Act of 1973. Public Law 93–222, 93rd Congress, 1st Session, December 29, 1973.

35. Dranove, *The Economic Evolution of American Health Care*, p. 67.

36. Jean Riedlinger, American Association of Health Plans, e-mail message to author, June 7, 2002.

37. *Employer Health Benefits 2001 Annual Survey, Market Share of Health Plans*, The Henry J. Kaiser Family Foundation, Section 6.

38. "16th Annual Mercer/Foster Higgins National Survey of Employer-Sponsored Health Plans," Mercer Human Resource Consulting. Available at *http://www.mercerhr.com/knowledgecenter/ reportdetail.jhtml?idContent=1051300.*

39. Dranove, *The Economic Evolution of American Health Care*, p. 162.

40. Dranove, *The Economic Evolution of American Health Care*, pp. 87-88.

41. "Physician Dissatisfaction with Medical Practice on the Rise," *Reuters Health*, July 20, 2001.

42. "Physician Dissatisfaction," July 20, 2001.

43. *Employer Health Benefits 2003 Annual Survey*, The Henry J. Kaiser Family Foundation, Exhibit 5.1.

44. M. Gregg Bloche and David M. Studdert, "A Quiet Revolution: Law as an Agent of Health System Change," *Health Affairs*, vol. 23, no. 2 (March/April 2004): 29-41.

Chapter Six

45. Lawrence H. Mirel, "We Call it Insurance, but That's Not Healthy," *Washington Post*, August 26, 2001.

46. Mirel, "We Call it Insurance, but That's Not Healthy," Aug. 26, 2001.

47. Quoted in Julie Appleby, "New Insurance Plans Turn Patients into Shoppers: Some Consumers Willing to Gamble They'll Stay Well," *USA Today*, January 8, 2002.

48. Personal communication to author, January 16, 2002.

49. Bradley J. Herring, "Does Access to Charity Care for the Uninsured Crowd Out Private Health Insurance Coverage?" (Working Paper, Yale University), September 7, 2001.

Chapter Seven

50. Milton Friedman, "How to Cure Health Care," *The Public Interest*, No. 142 (Winter 2001): 3-30.

51. Robert J. Mills, US Census Bureau, "Health Insurance Coverage: 2000," *Current Population Reports* (September 2002): 60–220.

52. "Health Plans Receive Positive Marks from Members," *Reuters Health*, January 16, 2002.

53. The 40 percent marginal rate, which includes 27 percent federal income tax, 7.65 percent combined tax for Social Security and Medicare, and 5.35 percent state income tax, is realistic for a family with an income greater than $45,000 a year. State income tax rates vary significantly.

54. "Higher HMO Premiums in Store," *Reuters Health*, July 26, 2001.

55. John Sheils and Randall Haught, "The Cost of Tax-Exempt Health Benefits in 2001," *Health Affairs*, Web Exclusive Publication, W4-106, February 25, 2004. Available digitally at *http://www.healthaffairs.org*.

56. Mirel, "We Call it Insurance, but That's Not Healthy," Aug. 26, 2001.

57. Goodman and Musgrave, *Patient Power*, p. vii.

58. Robert J. Mills, US Census Bureau, "Health Insurance Coverage: 2001," *Current Population Reports* (September 2002): 60-220.

59. See, for example, Kaiser Commission on Medicaid and the Uninsured, *The Uninsured and Their Access to Health Care*, The Henry J. Kaiser Family Foundation, January 2003

60. Mills, US Census Bureau, "Health Insurance Coverage: 2001."

61. "2002 Employer Health Benefits Survey," The Henry J. Kaiser Family Foundation and Health Research and Educational Trust (September 2002). Available at *www.kff.org.*

62. "2002 Employer Health Benefits Survey."

63. Sheils and Haught, "The Cost of Tax-Exempt Health Benefits in 2001."

64. Sheils and Haught, "The Cost of Tax-Exempt Health Benefits in 2001." Web Exclusive Publication W4-106.

Chapter Eight

65. "Working Capital," *Wall Street Journal,* April 24, 2002.

66. Stuart M. Butler, "Right Diagnosis, Wrong Prescription," *Health Affairs*, vol. 21, no. 4 (July/August 2002): 101.

67. Jonathan Gruber, "Taxes and Health Insurance," *National Bureau of Economic Research* (NBER Working Paper no. w8657), December 2001.

Chapter Nine

68. See Steffie Woolhandler and David U. Himmelstein, "Paying for National Health Insurance—And Not Getting It," *Health Affairs*, vol. 21, no. 4 (July/August 2002).

69. Stuart M. Butler, "Right Diagnosis, Wrong Prescription," *Health Affairs*, vol. 21, no. 4 (July/August 2002).

Chapter Ten

70. To obtain cash benefits from Social Security, seniors must enroll in Medicare Part A, which means they cannot carry private insurance. Many seniors want their social security benefits and would like to enroll in private insurance plans, but cannot because of the way Medicare was set up. See Blevins, *Medicare's Midlife Crisis*, pp. 10-11.

71. Marcia Angell, "A Wrong Turn on Patients' Rights," *New York Times*, June 23, 2001.

72. *An Analysis of the President's Budgetary Proposals for Fiscal Year 2001* (Washington, DC: Congressional Budget Office, April 2000): 47-49. Available at *ftp://ftp.cbo.gov/19xx/doc1908/pb0400.pdf*.

73. Blevins, *Medicare's Midlife Crisis*, pp. 25-35.

74. Blevins, *Medicare's Midlife Crisis*, p. 35.

75. Blevins, *Medicare's Midlife Crisis*, pp. 36-38.

76. Blevins, *Medicare's Midlife Crisis*, p. 36.

77. *2004 Annual Report of the Boards of Trustees of the Federal Hospital Insurance and Federal Supplementary Medical Insurance Trust Funds*, p. 2.

78. Blevins, *Medicare's Midlife Crisis*, p. 42.

79. General Accounting Office, "Medigap Insurance: Plans Are Widely Available but Have Limited Benefits and May Have High Costs," July 2001, GAO-01-941.

80. Feldman, *American Health Care*, p. 49.

81. David Gross and Normandy Brangan, "Out-of-Pocket Spending on Health Care By Medicare Beneficiaries Age 65 and Older: 1999 Projections," AARP Public Policy Institute, December 1999. Available at *http://research.aarp.org/health/ib41_hspend.pdf*.

82. Robert E. Moffit, Timothy Blanchard, Susan Bartlett Foote, and William G. Plested, "How Medicare Bureaucracy Limits the Range of Medical Treatment Available to Seniors," The Heritage Foundation, Heritage Lectures No. 666 (May 12, 2000): 3

83. Moffit *et al.*, "How Medicare Bureaucracy Limits the Range of Medical Treatment," p. 10.

84. Moffit *et al.*, "How Medicare Bureaucracy Limits the Range of Medical Treatment," p. 10.

85. Grace-Marie Arnett, Jonathan Emord, Lawrence Huntoon, and Robert Charrow, "How Medicare Paperwork Abuses Doctors and Harms Patients," The Heritage Foundation, Heritage Lectures No. 665 (May 11, 2000): 11.

86. Robert E. Moffit, "Importing HCFA-Style Regulation Into the Private Sector Through the Patients' Bill of Rights," The Heritage Foundation, WebMemo No. 18 (June 27, 2001). Available at *http://www.heritage.org/Research/HealthCare/WM18.cfm*.

87. American Hospital Association letter to Office of Information and Regulatory Affairs, Office and Management and Budget, May 28, 2003. Available online at *www.hospitalconnect.com*.

88. Moffit, "Importing HCFA-Style Regulation Into the Private Sector Through the Patients' Bill of Rights,"

89. Arnett *et al.*, "How Medicare Paperwork Abuses Doctors and Harms Patients," p. 5.

90. Blevins, "Medicare's Midlife Crisis," p. 55.

91. Blevins, "Medicare's Midlife Crisis," p. 49.

92. Goodman and Musgrave, *Patient Power*, p. 306.

93. Arnett *et al.*, "How Medicare Paperwork Abuses Doctors and Harms Patients," p. 18-19.

94. Pear, "Doctors Shunning Patients with Medicare."

95. Pear, "Doctors Shunning Patients with Medicare."

Chapter Eleven

96. Margaret Popper, "They Really Were Golden Years," *Business Week Online*, July 22, 2002.

97. US Census Bureau, "Statistical Abstract of the United States: 2003," No. 709.

98. Bernadette D. Proctor and Joseph Palakar, *Poverty in the United States: 2002*, Current Population Reports, US Census Bureau (September 2003): 60-222.

99. Popper, "They Really Were Golden Years."

100. "The Medicare + Choice Program in 2001 and 2002," Centers for Medicare and Medicaid Services, August 29, 2001.

101. Health Care Financing Administration, "Perceptions of the Medicare Population," (Health Care Financing Administration, 1999), Table 5.14. See also Cynthia G. Tudor, Gerald Riley, and Melvin Ingber, "Medicare Beneficiaries Perceptions of Care: A Comparison of Managed Care Enrollees to Fee-for-service Beneficiaries Using Data from the Medicare Current Beneficiary Survey." Available digitally at *http://www.academyhealth.org/abstracts/1997/tudor2.htm*.

102. "Protecting Medicare Beneficiaries When Their Medicare + Choice Organization Withdraws," Centers for Medicare and Medicaid Services, September 26, 2002.

103. Quoted in Yvonne Condes, "Thousands of Seniors Dropped from Medicare HMO," *Contra Costa Times*, October 5, 2001.

Chapter Twelve

104. Raymond Hernandez and Robert Pear, "State Officials are Cautious on Medicare Drug Benefit," *New York Times*, January 4, 2004.

105. "State Measures to Control Drug Costs, Access Reach Fever Pitch," Reuters, April 3, 2002.

106. See Frank Lichtenberg, "Benefits and Costs of Newer Drugs: An Update," National Bureau of Economic Research (Working Paper 8996), June 2002.

107. "2003 Annual Report of the Boards of Trustees of the Federal Hospital Insurance and Federal Supplementary Medical Insurance Trust Funds," Washington, DC, March 17, 2003.

108. Thomas R. Saving, "Creating a Market for Sick People," presentation at *Health Care Crises Facing Our Nation Today: Strategies for Reform*, American Enterprise Institute, March 24, 2003.

109. F.M. Scherer, "The Link Between Gross Profitability And Pharmaceutical R&D Spending," *Health Affairs*, Vol. 20, No. 5 (September/October 2001): 216-220.

110. PhRMA, "Profile Pharmaceutical Industry, 2004," Figure 1.3, p. 7.

111. US General Accounting Office, "Prescription Drugs: Expanding Access to Federal Prices Could Cause Other Price Changes," GAO/HEHS-00-118, August 2000.

Chapter Thirteen

112. United States Office of Personnel Management, "2003 FEHB Premiums." Available at *http://www.opm.gov/insure/health/03rates/index.asp*.

113. Leighton Ku, "How Many Low-Income Medicare Beneficiaries in each State Would be Denied the Medicare Prescription Drug Benefit under the Senate Drug Bill?" Center on Budget and Policy Priorities, July 31, 2003.

114. Christopher J. Gearon, "State-by-State, Plan-by-Plan List of Pharmacy Assistance Programs," AARP Web Exclusive (May 2004). Available digitally at *http://www.aarp.org/bulletin/yourmoney/Articles/statebystate.html*. (Accessed July 5, 2004).

115. Gearon, "State-by-State, Plan-by-Plan List of Pharmacy Assistance Programs."

116. Gearon, "State-by-State, Plan-by-Plan List of Pharmacy Assistance Programs."

Chapter Fourteen

117. Quoted in Jennifer Steinhauer, "Health Care: The Sound and the Fury," *New York Times*, December 16, 2001.

118. Julie A. Jacobs, "How Tough is Life? One State Has the Facts and Figures," *American Medical News*, August 13, 2001.

119. Robert F. St. Peter, Marie C. Reed, Peter Kemper, and David Blumenthal, "Changes in the Scope of Care Provided by Primary Care Physicians," *New England Journal of Medicine* 341 No. 26 (December 23, 1999): 1980-5.

120. Quoted in Pam Belluck, "Doctors' New Practices Offer Deluxe Service for Deluxe Fee," *New York Times*, January 15, 2002.

121. Survey of Physicians and Nurses (July 1999), The Henry J. Kaiser Family Foundation/Harvard School of Public Health.

Chapter Fifteen

122. "16th Annual Mercer/Foster Higgins National Survey of Employer-Sponsored Health Plans," Mercer Human Resource Consulting.

123. Patricia Butler, "Key Characteristics of State Managed Care Organization Liability Laws: Current Status and Experience" (August 2001), The Henry J. Kaiser Family Foundation.

124. "Health care Costs Rise 11% For Employers, Survey Finds," *Wall Street Journal*, September 7, 2001.

125. Stephen Barr, "Fed Workers Face Hike in Health Insurance Premiums," *Washington Post*, September 21, 2001.

126. Barbara Martinez, "Stiff Premiums for HMO Plans Surprise Benefits Managers Braced for Increases," *Wall Street Journal*, July 30, 2001.

Chapter Sixteen

127. Bill Sammon, "Can Lady's Dignity at Stake, Gore Says," *Washington Times*, October 19, 2000.

128. US Department of Labor, Bureau of Labor Statistics, *Consumer Expenditure Survey, 2001*, Table 3.

129. US Department of Labor, *Consumer Expenditure Survey, 2001*, Table 3.

130. Quoted in "Prescription Drug Spending up 18% in 2000; Fifth Straight Year of Increases," *Reuters Health*, May 4, 2001

131. "National Health Expenditures by Type of Service and Source of Funds: Calendar Years 1960–2000," Centers for Medicare and Medicaid Services.

132. Roger D. Feldman, ed., *American Health Care: Government, Market Processes, and the Public Interest,* (Oakland, CA: The Independent Institute, 2000): 49-51.

133. Center for Medicare & Medicaid Services, "Historical National Health Expenditures by Type of Service and Source of Funds: Calendar Years 1960-2002." Available at *http://www.cms.hhs.gov/statistics/ nhe/default.asp#business.*

134. Center for Medicare & Medicaid Services, "Historical National Health Expenditures by Type of Service and Source of Funds."

135. John Carey and Amy Barrett, "Drug Prices: What's Fair?" *Business Week*, December 10, 2001.

136. John E. Calfee, *Prices, Markets, and the Pharmaceutical Revolution* (Washington, DC: AEI Press, 2000): 61.

137. Calfee, *Prices, Markets, and the Pharmaceutical Revolution*, p. 23.

138. Bailey, "Goddam the Pusher Man."

139. Bailey, "Goddam the Pusher Man."

140. Bailey, "Goddam the Pusher Man."

141. Frank R. Lichtenberg, "The Benefits of New Drugs," *Economic Realities in Health Care Policy*, vol. 2, issue 2 (April 2002).

142. Calfee, *Prices, Markets, and the Pharmaceutical Revolution*, p. 10.

143. Calfee, *Prices, Markets, and the Pharmaceutical Revolution*, p. 10.

144. Bailey, "Goddam the Pusher Man."

145. Frank R. Lichtenberg, "Benefits and Costs of Newer Drugs: An Update," *National Bureau of Economic Research* (Working Paper 8996), June 2002.

146. Martin Zelder, "Spend More, Wait Less? The Myth of Underfunded Medicare," *Fraser Forum* (August 2000).

147. Calfee, *Prices, Markets, and the Pharmaceutical Revolution*, p. 17.

148. Masia, "Pharmaceutical Innovation."

149. Merrill Matthews Jr., "Answering Peter Jennings and ABC on Prescription Drugs," The Galen Institute, May 31, 2002.

150. Matthews, "Answering Peter Jennings."

151. Matthews, "Answering Peter Jennings."

152. *Fortune*, April 14, 2003, p. F-59.

153. *Fortune*, April 14, 2003, and Matthews, "Answering Peter Jennings."

154. Matthews, "Answering Peter Jennings."

155. "Total Cost to Develop a New Prescription Drug, Including Cost of Post-Approval Research, Is $897 Million," News Release, Tufts Center for the Study of Drug Development, May 13, 2003.

156. "The Drug Discovery, Development and Approval Process," Independent Institute. Available digitally at *http://www.fdareview.org/graphics/graph1.jpg.*

157. Gardiner Harris, "Why Drug Makers are Failing in Quest for New Blockbusters," *Wall Street Journal*, April 18, 2002.

158. Harris, "Why Drug Makers are Failing in Quest for New Blockbusters."

159. "The Drug Discovery, Development and Approval Process."

160. Pharmaceutical Research and Manufacturers of America (PhRMA), *Pharmaceutical Industry Profile 2003* (Washington, DC: PhRMA, 2003).

161. F.M. Scherer, "The Link Between Gross Profitability And Pharmaceutical R&D Spending," *Health Affairs*, vol. 20, no. 5 (September/October 2001): 216–220.

162. Holman W. Jenkins, Jr., "Peter Jennings on Drugs," *Wall Street Journal*, June 5, 2002.

163. Jenkins, "Peter Jennings on Drugs."

164. Jenkins, "Peter Jennings on Drugs."

Chapter Seventeen

165. "Pharmacists and Benefit Managers Square Off Over Pharmacy Benefit Regulations," *Reuters Health*, June 25, 2002.

166. Tara Parker-Pope, "Many Doctors Aren't Aware of Alternative Drug Choices," *Wall Street Journal*, September 7, 2001.

167. Henry I. Miller, "Can Dr. McClellan Cure the FDA?" *Hoover Digest*, 2004, No. 1.

168. Tufts Center for the Study of Drug Development, *Outlook 2004*, p. 2.

169. Tufts Center for the Study of Drug Development, "Tufts CSDD Quantifies Savings from Boosting New Drug R&D Efficiency," *Impact Report*, vol. 4, no. 5, September/October 2002.

170. Parker-Pope, "Many Doctors Aren't Aware."

171. Ceci Connolly, "Claritin to Be Sold Over the Counter," *Washington Post*, March 9, 2002.

172. Milt Freudenheim, "Claritin's Price Falls, but Drug Costs More," *New York Times*, May 8, 2003.

173. Freudenheim, "Claritin's Price Falls."

Chapter Eighteen

174. John R. Graham, "Prescription Drug Prices in Canada and the United States—Part 3: Retail Price Distribution," *Public Policy Sources* no. 50 (August 2001) (Vancouver: The Fraser Institute), p. 7.

175. Petti Fong, "White Rock MDs to Open American-Only Clinic," *Vancouver Sun*, August 10, 2000.

176. Tamsin Carlisle, "Canada Cools to US Drug Flow," *Wall Street Journal*, December 26, 2003.

177. Robert Pear, "Plan to Import Drugs From Canada Passes in Senate," *New York Times*, July 18, 2002.

178. Quoted in "Sure, Cheap Canadian Drugs," *Wall Street Journal*, July 23, 2002.

Chapter Nineteen

179. David Dial, et al., *Tort Excess 2004: The Necessity for Reform from a Policy, Legal and Risk Management Perspective*, The Insurance Information Institute, *http://www.iii.org/media/hottopics/insurance/liability/tort/*.

180. *US Tort Costs: 2003 Update, Trends and Findings on the Costs of the US Tort System*, Tillinghast-Towers Perrin, p. 16.

181. US Department of Labor, Bureau of Labor Statistics, "US Consumer Expenditure Survey 2002," Table 3.

182. *Medical Malpractice*, The Insurance Information Institute, February 2004. Available digitally at *http://www.iii.org/media/hottopics/insurance/medicalmal/*. (Accessed May 4, 2004.)

183. "Limiting Tort Liability for Medical Malpractice," Congressional Budget Office, January 8, 2004.

184. "Medical Malpractice Insurance: Multiple Factors Have Contributed to Increased Premium Rates," General Accounting Office, June 2003, GAO-03-702.

185. "Medical Malpractice Insurance," GAO, June 2003.

186. "Addressing the Medical Malpractice Insurance Crisis," National Governors Association, December 5, 2002.

187. "Confronting the New Health Care Crisis: Improving Health Care Quality and Lowering Costs by Fixing Our Medical Malpractice Liability System," US Department of Health and Human Services, July 24, 2002.

188. "Confronting the New Health Care Crisis," July 24, 2002.

189. "Confronting the New Health Care Crisis," July 24, 2002.

190. "Medical Malpractice," *Hot Topics & Insurance Issues*, The Insurance Information Institute, February 2004.

191. "Confronting the New Health Care Crisis," HHS, July 24, 2002.

192. Robert P. Hartwig and Claire Wilkinson, *Medical Malpractice Insurance*, The Insurance Information Institute, June 2003.

193. H.R. 4280. Help Efficient, Accessible, Low-cost, Timely Healthcare (HEALTH) Act of 2004, sponsored by Rep. James C. Greenwood, (R-PA), introduced in House on May 5, 2004.

194. "Limiting Tort Liability for Medical Malpractice," Congressional Budget Office, January 8, 2004.

Chapter Twenty

195. Regina E. Herzlinger, *Market Driven Health Care: Who Wins, Who Loses in the Transformation of America's Largest Service Industry* (New York: Addison-Wesley, 1997), p. xxi.

196. Humphrey Taylor, "Cyberchondriacs Update," *The Harris Poll #21*, May 1, 2002.

197. Robert W. Secor, "How I Get Home in Time for Dinner: Tired of Wwolfing Down Meals and Working Late, the Author Decided to Do Something About It. His Solution May Surprise You," *Medical Economics*, August 23, 2002.

198. Victoria Rouch, "Most Patients Seek Relief with Alternative Therapies," *Morning Star* (Wilmington NC), June 3, 2002.

199. Eileen Beal, "Considering the Alternatives, Greater Number of Care Providers Integrating Nontraditional Treatments," *Crain's Cleveland Business*, March 4, 2002.

200. See *An Employer's Guide to Consumer Directed Health care Approaches*, Wye River Group on Health Care, October 2001.

201. Greg Scandlen, *Defined Contribution Health Insurance*, National Center for Policy Analysis, Policy Backgrounder No. 154, October 26, 2000.

202. The Kaiser Family Foundation and Health Research and Educational Trust, "Employer Health Benefits: 2002 Annual Survey," Exhibit 4.12. Available digitally at *http://www.kff.org/content/2002/3251/3251-section4.pdf*.

203. Scandlen, *Defined Contribution Health Insurance*, NCPA, October 26, 2000.

204. Scandlen, *Defined Contribution Health Insurance*, NCPA, October 26, 2000.

Chapter Twenty-One

205. Victoria C. Bunce, *Medical Savings Accounts: Progress and Problems under HIPAA*, Cato Institute Policy Analysis No. 411 (August 8, 2001), pp. 8-9.

206. Marc L. Berk and Alan C. Monheit, "The Concentration of Health Care Expenditures, Revisited," *Health Affairs*, Vol. 20, No. 2 (March/April 2001), Exhibit 1.

207. Bunce, *Medical Savings Accounts*, p. 5.

208. Bunce, *Medical Savings Accounts*, pp. 23-27.

209. Ron Lieber, "New Way to Curb Medical Costs: Make Employees Feel the Sting," *The Wall Street Journal*, June 23, 2004, p. 1.

210. Lieber, "New Way to Curb Medical Costs," p. 28.

211. Public Law 104–191, Health Insurance Portability and Accountability Act of 1996, 104th Congress.

212. Internal Revenue Service, "Archer MSAs," *Medical Savings Accounts (MSAs)*, Publication 969. Available digitally at *http://www.irs.gov/pub/irs-pdf/p969.pdf*, July 30, 2003.

213. Public Law 104–191, Health Insurance Portability and Accountability Act of 1996.

214. Bunce, *Medical Savings Accounts*, p. 13.

Chapter Twenty-Two

215. Dranove, *The Economic Evolution of American Health Care*, pp. 87-88.

216. Pam Belluck, "Doctors' New Practices Offer Deluxe Service for Deluxe Fee," *New York Times*, January 15, 2002.

217. See Liz Kowalczyk, "For $4,000, Doctor's Devotion 2 Boston Internists to Offer More Access," *Boston Globe*, December 13, 2001; Pam Belluck, "Doctors' New Practices Offer Deluxe Service for Deluxe Fee," *New York Times*, January 15, 2002; Eileen McNamara, "Devotion to Themselves: Steven Flier and Jordan Busch Personify the Hippocratic Oath," *Boston Globe*, December 16, 2001.

218. John D. Goodson, letter to *Boston Globe*, December 18, 2001.

219. Liz Kowalczyk, "Tufts Health Raises Concerns on 'Premium Practice' by Doctors," *Boston Globe*, December 20, 2001.

220. Belluck, "Doctors' New Practices Offer Deluxe Service for Deluxe Fee."

221. "Premium Practices: Lawmakers ask Thompson to Investigate," *American Health Line*, March 5, 2002; Neil Versel, "Do VIP practices upcharge Medicare?," *Modern Physician*, May 1, 2002; "Lawmakers Say 'Concierge' Physician Practices could Violate Medicare Law," *Reuters Health Information*, March 5, 2002.

222. Ceci Connolly, "The Wealth Care System: When CEOs and VIPs Need Health Care, They Get the Best Money Can Buy," *Washington Post*, May 28, 2002.

223. Quoted in Christine Wiebe, "Boutique Doctors Cater to Patients' Needs," *Medscape Money & Medicine*, 3(1) (2002).

224. Devin Friedman, "Dr. Levine's Dilemma," *New York Times Magazine*, May 5, 2002.

225. Milton Friedman, Speech to the Club for Growth, San Francisco, CA, July 2001.

226. Nancy Shute, "That Old-time Medicine," *US News & World Report*, April 22, 2002.

227. Quoted in Shute, "That Old-time Medicine."

228. Gina Kolata, "Cheaper Body Scans Spread, Despite Doubts," *New York Times*, May 27, 2002.

229. Kolata, "Cheaper Body Scans Spread," May 27, 2002.

230. Kolata, "Cheaper Body Scans Spread," May 27, 2002.

231. Quoted in Kolata, "Cheaper Body Scans Spread," May 27, 2002.

232. "Union's Move to Mail-order Prescriptions Ignites Controversy," *Reuters Medical News*, April 5, 2002.

233. Steven Greenhouse, "Pharmacists Attack Union Over Prescriptions By Mail," *New York Times*, March 28, 2002.

234. Michelle Andrews, "Here Are Your Pills. Do You Want the Seminar?" *New York Times*, June 16, 2002.

235. Andrews, "Here Are Your Pills."

236. Michael E. Porter and Elizabeth Olmsted Teisberg, "Redefining Competition in Health Care," *Harvard Business Review* (June 2004): 65-76.

237. Shute, "That Old-time Medicine," April 22, 2002.

238. A.M. House and J.M. Roberts, "Telemedicine in Canada," *Canadian Medical Association Journal*, 117(4) (1977): 386-8.

239. Ace Allen and Astara March, "Telemedicine at the Community Cancer Center," *Oncology Issues*, 17(1) (2002): 18-24.

240. Allen and March, "Telemedicine at the Community Cancer Center."

241. Quoted in Allen and March, "Telemedicine at the Community Cancer Center."

Part Two

The Canadian Solution: Legalize Competition

INTRODUCTION:
Canada's Health Care Conundrum

Canadians like nothing better than to praise their health care system, and contrast it with the United States. "For Canadians, our publicly funded health care system is a key distinguishing characteristic for our country," noted a September 2001 report from the Canadian Senate. "In fact, it has achieved iconic status. It is perceived to reflect Canadian values and these are seen to stand in sharp contrast to the values of our American neighbors."[1]

The ability to insure 100 percent of the population, while spending less than their neighbors south of the border, is a genuine source of pride for Canadians. However, Canadians are finding themselves facing constraints and controversies similar to those inherent in the US health care system. As in the United States, health care in Canada faces its largest constraints in terms of affordability. Because health care is provided by a government-run, single-payer system, it is the Canadian patient who ultimately pays the price in terms of access and quality.

Despite obvious differences, the US and Canadian systems are growing to resemble one another in their shortcomings. What these two countries share (and many other countries, for that matter) is too much government, too much bureaucracy, and too many regulations and mandates.

Third-party payment for health care services is a serious problem in both the United States and Canada. Third-party decision-making is a bigger problem still. Governments and employers make far too many health care decisions on behalf of citizens. Nobel laureate economist Milton Friedman often says that "nobody spends somebody else's money as wisely or as frugally as he spends his own."[2]

The solution in Canada is to open up the system to competitive improvements, and to grant Canadians the power to choose between different health care plans.

CHAPTER ONE:
What is the Single-payer System?

The single-payer in Canada is the government. The advertised virtue of a single-payer system is that it eliminates the costs of having multiple payers, many of them private-sector entities that must reward investors, and the need to spend money on marketing budgets and overhead costs that are often redundant.

Canadian governments maintain complete control of health insurance for the hospital and physician sectors of the health care system through "medicare," a jointly administered program of the federal and provincial governments. Although often referred to as a "single-payer system," it is really a series of single-payer systems.

Unlike in Britain, for example, where the government actually runs many health facilities, the majority of hospitals and doctors' offices in Canada are nominally independent of the government. But considering that the government is the only funding source allowed by law, this independence is more theoretical than practical.

In fact, Canada is the only Western country in which private insurance for publicly-insured procedures is actually outlawed.[3]

Here's how it works in practice: Through medicare, the federal government sets and administers the national principles and standards for provincial health care, as currently defined by the Canada Health Act. It transfers federal funds to provincial governments for health care and social services through the Canada Health and Social Transfer Act (CHST). Provincial governments are required to contribute significant financial support to their hospital and medical insurance programs. They are also responsible for administering the programs.

Governments pay for just under 70 percent of total spending for health care nationally. Canadians finance the remainder of health care spending privately through supplementary health insurance, employer-sponsored health care benefits, or out-of-pocket payments for services that are not covered by medicare.

The dollars actually spent by Canadian consumers on health care in Canada, however, are low enough for those consumers to be shielded from the real costs of health care. Canadian medicare resembles US Medicaid more than it resembles US Medicare, where seniors must pay significant co-pays. Like Medicaid, Canadian medicare is run by provincial governments, with partial funding and oversight by the federal government.

In their *Harvard Business Review* article, "Redefining Competition in Health Care," authors Michael Porter and Elizabeth Olmsted Teisberg say that the "wrong kinds of competition have made a mess of the American health care system. The right kinds of competition can straighten it out."

They do not see the Canadian single-payer model as the answer to the dilemmas facing the US system. They eloquently point out that:

> A single-payer system, which has been proposed, would end the practice of excluding high-risk subscribers. But it would only exacerbate all the other skewed incentives by eliminating competition at the level of health plans and giving the payer more bargaining power with which to shift costs to providers, patients, and employers. A single payer would have greater incentive to reduce its costs by restricting or rationing services and slowing the diffusion of innovation. The only real solution is to change these incentives and open up competition, not to make health insurance a government monopoly."[4]

CHAPTER TWO:
How does Canada's Single-payer System Differ from Universal Coverage?

In everyday usage, "universal coverage" is often used synonymously with a government-run "single-payer" system that provides every resident with an insurance package. However, universal coverage does not require the government to monopolize the financing of the preponderance of health care. If the coverage is to be taken literally, as in insurance coverage, systems of competing and complimentary private and public payers could be established to ensure that every resident has recourse to a third-party payer for critical medical services.

If, as is often the case when politicians invoke it, universal coverage means that every person has access to quality medical treatment in a timely fashion, it can be achieved without total third-party coverage. In fact, if the latter definition is the goal, single-payer systems can actually work against universal coverage for many treatments. Canada's single-payer system entails broad aspects of social control that make it more of an intrusive, centrally-directed method than the simple provision of coverage for all people.

Under single-payer, the government controls the funds and, therefore, makes every important decision about the provision of health care. Because benefits and premiums are the same for

Some Americans continue to embrace proposals to adopt a
Canadian-style health care system for all. "Like every other
advanced country, we need a single-payer or consolidated-payer
system to prevent both the widespread underinsurance and the
cost-shifting," former editor of the New England Journal of
Medicine and senior lecturer at Harvard Medical School Marcia
Angell wrote in The American Prospect.[a]

Angell is a spokesperson for Physicians for a National Health
Program, a group of about 8,000 physicians within the American
Medical Association (AMA) that collaborates with liberal
members of Congress to keep single-payer legislation always in
Congress. Activist groups work tirelessly to get single-payer
programs passed at the state level.

California State Senator Sheila Kuehl has sponsored a
single-payer bill that was passed by the California Senate in the
late spring of 2003.[b] It was placed on hold during the recall of
Governor Davis; it is expected that Senator Kuehl will
re-introduce the legislation in fall 2004. In Maine, the legislature
created and funded a bureaucracy to study the feasibility of
implementing a single-payer system.

But when Americans actually get the chance to vote on
single-payer proposals, they register distaste. In 1996, California
voters rejected a single-payer initiative. Oregon voters did the
same in 2002.

(Sources: [a]Marcia Angell, "Placebo Politics: Health Care Reform
Requires Strong Medicine; The Election-year Rhetoric Makes Us
Feel Better—But It Is Deferring a Real Cure," American Prospect
(November 6, 2000): 25.

[b]Timm Herdt, "Lawmakers Vote on Flurry of Bills: Heavy Action
at Session's Halfway Point," Ventura County Star, June 7, 2003.)

everyone, consumers have no ability to make smart health care purchases. The decisions are made for them.

Under single-payer, consumers are expected to be passive. They should not expect innovations in health care. Even today, Canadian entrepreneurs are often prevented from creating specialized medical sites that promote efficiency and reduce costs. These attempts are criticized for "stealing" customers from established hospitals. "Sympathetic politicians now respond to (such) charges by enforcing Certificate of Need laws that curtail specialty orthopedic and heart facilities, despite ample evidence of the better quality health care they provide—at lower cost," writes Harvard Business School professor Regina Herzlinger.[5]

Canadians are proud of this system. But today this pride is increasingly harmful to the health of Canadians. While Canada is busy studying its health care system, most innovations—medical, pharmaceutical, technological, and even policy—are happening elsewhere. It is Canada's turn to play catch up.

CHAPTER THREE:
How Did the Canadian System Come to Be?

> The first function of the founders of nations, after founding itself, is to devise a set of true falsehoods about origins—a mythology—that will make it desirable for nationals to live under a common authority, and, indeed make it impossible to entertain contrary thoughts.
> —Forrest McDonald[6]

Triumphant tales of the Canadian single-payer health care system often start in 1910 in Scotland, where a six-year-old boy named Tommy Douglas suffered a cut to his leg that wouldn't heal. Douglas later moved to Canada, where a surgeon looking to try out a new procedure saved him from a hospital charity ward and almost certain amputation. "That cut changed Canadian history," wrote Canadian academics and health care activists Pat and Hugh Armstrong.[7]

While recovering in the hospital, little Tommy Douglas did not conclude that it was a good thing that the private economy produced enough wealth to make such generous charity possible. Rather, he concluded that governments ought to make such charity unnecessary by funding universal health care.

From here, the story fast-forwards to 1946 and the province of Saskatchewan. Douglas, now the province's socialist premier, leads an effort to pass government-funded hospital insurance for every Saskatchewan resident. The effort is so successful that the federal government passes its own program in 1957. Douglas's work, however, was not yet complete. In 1961 he proposed, and Saskatchewan's parliament passed, full-fledged government medical insurance.

Doctors at first resisted, and went on strike. But they soon relented.

In 1966, the Canadian Parliament in Ottawa passed national legislation that provided money to provinces that followed Saskatchewan's lead. By 1968, all of them had done just that and passed programs of government insurance. This system has been a source of pride for many Canadians ever since.

As Maclean's surveys have shown consistently over the years, medicare is a matter of enormous pride for many Canadians, rivaling the Maple Leaf flag as a symbol. With medicare playing such a central role in Canadian life, it is sometimes hard to imagine that it has been in effect for only about three decades of Canada's 133 years."
(Source: Robert Marshall, "Paying the Price: User Fees and Two-tier. Are Canadians Ready for Fundamental Changes to Health Care?" Maclean's, January 1, 2001.)

"For more than twenty years," write Michael Rachlis, MD, and Carol Kushner, two leading analysts of the Canadian system, "Canada has been a world leader in health policy, enriching the field with new conceptual models to help improve our understanding of health and health care."[8]

As McDonald notes, all societies need their founding myths. The same can be said of large institutions and systems, especially those that create the identity of a nation. And few would deny that a significant amount of Canadian identity is wrapped up in its medicare program.

Like most expansions of the state, the expansion of single-payer relied on two dynamics. First, Canadians consciously employed the incremental strategies of building one program on the success of the last. People liked government-provided hospital insurance in Saskatchewan, which led others to be eager to implement it in their provinces, and, eventually, nationwide.

The second dynamic is largely invisible to the public. As we've seen time and again in the United States, politicians build new programs on the failings of past ones. Government failure, in other words, provides the justification for more government.

Here's how it has worked in Canada. In 1948, the Canadian federal government decided the country needed more hospitals, and started funding the building of hospitals.

Hospitals are expensive, not only to build, but to run. At the same time, the provinces, which were adopting socialized hospital insurance programs, discovered that paying for hospitals was much more expensive than they had predicted.

So in 1957, four years before Douglas's second triumph, the Canadian Parliament passed an act that provided provinces with money for hospital insurance programs. This, too, bore unintended consequences, not the least of which was shifting even more care out of the home and doctor's office to the hospital, the most expensive of all locations.[9]

This shift to hospitals provides the context for understanding Douglas's second foundational act, the creation of socialized medical insurance in 1961. As with hospital insurance, Douglas's legislation was imitated in other provinces, then by the federal government. The push for medical insurance is but one episode in a familiar and relentless pattern that continues to this day: the government is still continuously being called in to fix problems caused by previous government action.

This drawn out dynamic—not the Saskatchewan founding moment—is the true story of Canada's once proud, now troubled, single-payer health care system.

Of course, Canada's system certainly appeared innovative in its day. One might say it was the original "third way." It rejected the models of its most kindred countries. Unlike Great Britain, where the government owned the hospitals and clinics, in Canada the hospitals and clinics, with a few exceptions, would neither be owned nor *directly* managed by any government.

But unlike the United States, where health care services were at the time largely left up to private arrangements, governments would pay for all medically necessary procedures. While the federal government would help fund the programs—originally on a dollar-to-dollar matching basis for hospital and physician services—provincial governments were charged with designing and operating the insurance systems.

The system was founded close to the peak of people's faith in governments to address societal problems. Government insurance, it was thought then (and is still widely asserted by many today), is more efficient than private insurance, because it wipes out wasteful competition. Allowing each province to run its own plan was a deft application of federalism. It allowed governments to tailor plans to local conditions and provided room for experimentation while still relying on federal support.

And while the government didn't directly own and operate hospitals, clinics, or doctors' offices, it was well understood that "he who pays the piper calls the tune." Having a single payer per province, then, would allow for rational planning of the system and eliminate wasteful spending. (This financial control would later shift significant power from the provinces to the federal government, which would dictate policy at the threat of withholding money.)

As for patients, planners actually believed that the price of care bore no relationship to the amount of care demanded. Lord Beveridge, a driving force behind the creation of Britain's socialized system, actually predicted in the decade Douglas enjoyed his first triumph that free universal access would in practice *decrease* demand for health care over time as people's needs were met.[10]

Few, if any, believe this now. The Canadian experience explains why. At first, everyone seemed to benefit from the Canadian system. Doctors, who protested its adoption, saw their incomes increase, as patients were free to spend their countrymen's tax money.

Saskatchewan doctors, for example, saw their incomes increase by more than one-third right after the government took over all insurance.[11] Hospitals, too, had a ready source of funding. Patients enjoyed free health care on demand. And all this cost less than the United States spent.

It seemed too good to be true—and it was.

It turns out that when health care is free, people do demand more of it, and they demand it at expensive places, such as hospital emergency rooms.

Thirty years ago, the average Canadian visited his doctor three times a year. Today, that patient will show up twice as often.[12]

Exploding demand drove up costs. The lack of competition kept the single-payer system from being able to manage its costs. To keep spending under control, the federal government reduced its share of total health care spending. Today, the federal government provides less than one-quarter of provincial health care budgets.

Provinces, in turn, cut payments to doctors, cut back on the services covered, and in the most drastic step of all, clamped down on hospital budgets and quashed the proliferation of high-tech equipment. At every juncture, governments responded in the same way: Quash private initiative and increase government control.

At first, doctors, in at least one province, Alberta, responded by billing patients directly for amounts greater than the government paid for insured services, a practice dubbed "extra billing." The federal government outlawed extra billing for insured services when it passed the Canada Health Act in 1984. Doctors again responded by billing for such uninsured services as phone calls and letter writing.[13] Costs kept going up.

Some provinces limited the total amount doctors could bill, and so they closed up shop at the end of each fiscal quarter and took vacations.[14] Finally, many left for the land South of Niagara, which offered not only warmer weather but also higher salaries and more professional freedom. Patients, at least those who wanted prompt specialized care, found themselves forced to follow the doctors' trail across the border.

What happened? Costs are properly conceived as the total amount of things—time, money, and alternative activities—one must give up to acquire a given good. In Canadian health care, these rising costs have been shifted from taxpayers, who pay in monetary form, to patients, who bear the non-monetary costs in increased pain and suffering, and monetary costs of lost wages or traveling to the United States for prompt treatment.

Today, after 30 years of government intervention, the system suffers from:

- long waiting times for critical procedures;
- lack of access to current technology;
- increasing costs to taxpayers and patients; and
- a brain drain of doctors

In turn, each of these problems has caused Canadians to lose out in their quest for the three essential aspects of any good health care system. Canadians are finding their health care degraded in terms of:

- access,
- affordability; and
- quality

Each of these problems can be traced to government intervention. So how do many of Canada's leading health care experts respond? They call for yet more government control and increased funding by raising taxes.

"Only tradition can explain why it is acceptable for government to decide how many teachers or police officers should serve a particular community at public expense," writes health analyst Jane Fulton, Ph.D., "but offensive when government applies the same principle to physicians."[15] Write Rachlis and Kushner in their widely read book, *Strong Medicine: How to Save Canada's Health Care System*, "A greater federal presence in health policy is essential."[16]

CHAPTER FOUR:
What does Canada Spend Every Year on Health Care? How Does the Canadian Health Care Debate Affect the United States?

For all the non-monetary costs the system shifts to patients, and for all the restrictions it places on expensive procedures, one would hope the system would at least control spending. Canada's system does allow it to exert some control over monetary costs.

Canadian health care costs 9.4 percent of that country's GDP, a level exceeded by three countries—Germany, Switzerland, and the United States.[17] Once one accounts for the relatively youthful population in Canada, [18] only the United States spends more on health care in total.[19]

Quantifying health care costs as a percent of GDP is highly dubious, however, because this statistic says nothing of the product being purchased, whether it's swift surgery when one needs it, or a place in line and a bottle of painkillers. And health care is not cheap for the average working Canadian. The bill is just buried in an already high tax burden.

Nor is it cheap for the provinces. When medicare was first passed, the federal government picked up about half the bill. Today, the national share is less than 25 percent.[20]

In Saskatchewan, medicare's birthplace, health care accounts for 40 percent of the province's budget. This is more than the province collects in personal income and the sales tax.[21] The average province spends nearly one in three budget dollars on health care.[22]

Still, the Canadian Medical Association (CMA) says that even these levels of break-the-bank spending aren't enough, and warns of a "cataclysmic collapse" if more money isn't pumped into patient care. Politicians are scrambling to shift the costs to others. In August 2001, provincial premiers, led by Ontario's then-premier Mike Harris, put the national government on notice that if it didn't pass down more money for health care, the provinces were prepared to ignore its regulations.[23]

> *Dr. David Gratzer figures that government-provided medicare costs working Canadians $.21 for every $1 earned. Writes Gratzer, "This means that Canadians earning $35,000 a year pay $7,350 for Medicare." (Source: Gratzer, Code Blue, p. 175.)*

Canada's relationship with the United States is complex, perhaps nowhere more so than in regard to health care. Canada often finds itself in the shadow of its more boisterous neighbor. Yet in health care, starting in the 1960s, it was Canada that boldly broke from the United States, applying what it considers its superior moral values—the idea that the state ought to take care of the individual.

For some time, when the government was willing to pump in ever-increasing sums of money, the Canadian system sparkled, causing even many Americans to long for such a system. Not yet a half century later, however, the system is showing numerous strains that, as we shall see in the final chapter, can only be alleviated by opening it up to market forces.

Few Canadians are fully aware of the extent of the growing crisis in Canadian health care. Every Canadian does know two things, however. First, health care is a right that ought to be guaranteed by government. Thankfully, an enlightened Canadian government sees to this right, even if exercising that right and securing care takes some time. Second, the United States has a horrible, private, profit-driven system that leaves millions without medical insurance.

The specter of the United States dominates Canadian health care thinking, paralyzing its policies, even as Canada increasingly relies on the United States as an integral part of its system. Thus, the United States plays many roles in the Canadian health care system, most prominently as its chief straw man, safety valve, and source of innovations. "In Canada," writes Fulton, "queuing is far more acceptable than the notion of rationing American-style, which leaves consumers with the decision of whether treatment is needed and worth the price of the user fee or other deterrent."[24]

> "A Canadian... measures Canada inevitably and overwhelmingly against the United States... This Canadian measuring produces a kaleidoscope of reactions, ranging from envy to anger, from inferiority complex to moral superiority, from doubt to defiance." (Source: Jeffrey Simpson, columnist, Globe and Mail and author, Star-Spangled Canadians: Canadians Living the American Dream (HarperCollins Canada, 2000), p. 6.)

Of course, this is a distorted view of health care in America, the health care equivalent of Americans considering the beer-swilling stars of Canadian Strange Brew, Bob and Doug McKenzie, as typical of their countrymen. Still, the negative image of the United States has a powerful grip on Canadian psychology, which fears destroying the system that's made it so proud and moving closer to the heartless US model.

There's no denying that the free-spending United States provides Canadians with many health care benefits. Thousands of Canadians travel south for prompt care, sometimes at government expense, which alleviates the need for Canadian governments to undertake the necessary reforms to supply these medical services domestically. As incredible as it may sound, some defenders of the Canadian system blame the United States for raising the expectations of Canadians.

"The Canadian system is already vulnerable to the workings of the US system," write Rachlis and Kushner, articulating this view. "The explosion of largely unevaluated US technology, driven by incentives for private profit, has created pressure for similar expansion here. Very high incomes for some American doctors—particularly surgeons—have put pressure on certain specialties in Canada. Both these factors are a strain on Canada's health budgets. Most important, will America's rejection of a Canadian-style health care system lead us to doubt the fundamental soundness of our own approach to health care financing?"[25]

In truth, Canadians already benefit from the considerable sums US companies sink into medical research. Although Canada's bureaucracies restrict the drugs its citizens have access to, the products that survive the screening are largely developed in the United States. And even as Canadians health experts point to administrative costs in the United States as a reason the Canadian system is superior, they admit to free-riding on US expenditures.

"A few years ago it appeared that Canada should concentrate on measuring the value of specific elements of health care," writes Fulton. "For two reasons, this is not the case. First, the United States is spending $1 billion annually on cost-effectiveness research and a great deal more is being done in Europe. Second, Canada has been slow to make use of the information available."[26]

There's an old joke that asks, "What's the definition of a Canadian?" The answer is, "An American who has health insurance and doesn't have a gun." In Toronto, this joke was tragically reversed on New Year's Day, 2000, when a father, frustrated that he couldn't get care for his extremely sick baby, pulled a gun on emergency room workers. He was shot and killed by police.[27]

Canadian critics, as the last chapter demonstrates, are correct that all is not well to the south. They are wrong, however, about how US problems relate to Canada. They are wrong to let fear of the shortcomings of the US approach to health care stop them from addressing Canada's problems. Above all, they are wrong in thinking that the source of the problems is a lack of government.

CHAPTER FIVE:
Can You Give Me Concrete Evidence of the Failure of Single-payer?

"Everybody waits."
—Anonymous Canadian surgeon.[28]

At a glance, Canada seems to have progressed past the US system, providing its citizens with universal health insurance while spending less than the United States. But beneath the shiny veneer of Canada's single-payer health-care system is a darker reality: old and inadequate equipment, intolerable waits for treatment, and disaffected physicians.

"In the past, we did the best we could for patients," Dr. Bill McArthur, a longtime veteran of Canadian health care, told fellow doctor and author David Gratzer. "Today we do the best we are allowed to do under the circumstances."[29]

Canadians once found few barriers to seeing a doctor for day-to-day conditions—a situation that sadly is no longer true. When they fall seriously ill, or a bug spreads through the Great White North, the system's life-threatening fissures actually become life threatening. Even something as routine and predictable as an outbreak of the flu can seriously disrupt emergency care and tax hospital capacity, leading to the neglect of acutely ill patients.

"No Hospital Beds in BC, Mom-to-be Flown to Alberta" read the headline on the front page of the May 29, 2004 edition of *The Vancouver Sun*. The article tells the story of the Cornthwaites, the parents of premature twin boys, who were born in Edmonton, Alberta, because no hospital in British Columbia could accept them. Mr. Cornthwaite accused BC "of having a Third World health system that puts lives at risk." He went on to criticize the BC health system for being so poorly managed that it could not find room for the birth of two babies in an emergency, adding "it took about seven hours to sort out the bureaucracy and get them on a flight to Alberta."

A flu outbreak in 1999 practically closed some hospitals to the most critically ill patients for, on average, more than three hours a day for twelve weeks. "In the 12 weeks beginning on Nov. 1, 1999," one report noted, "York Central hospital was on critical care bypass—rejecting even the most needy patients—for 268 hours. For the entire previous year the total was 10.5 hours." (Source: Robert Sheppard, "Stress in Suburbia," Maclean's, February 7, 2000.)

An outbreak of *Clostridium difficile* caused the death of as many as 100 patients at University Hospital in Sherbrooke, Quebec, over an 18-month span starting in 2003 and continuing through 2004. Nearly 90 more patients have died due to the bacterial agent at other hospitals in Montreal and Calgary. Dr. Jacques Pepin, who authored a study on the outbreak for the *Canadian Medical Association Journal*, places some of the blame on deteriorating conditions of Canadian hospitals that can leave up to 40 patients sharing a single bathroom. "[I]n some of these old buildings, the sanitary conditions are intolerable," Dr. Pepin told *The Canadian Press*. "I mean it's indecent." [30] That was certainly the experience reported by Lysiane Gagnon, who wrote to *The Globe and Mail* about accompanying her mother to a hospital for two cataract operations. "The facilities were cramped and somewhat seedy," wrote Gagnon. "Both times, my mother had to change in the unisex bathroom off the waiting room, with her clothes balanced on the sink, near a toilet that the previous occupant had not bothered to flush."[31]

The flu of 1999 was a prelude to the Severe Acute Respiratory
Syndrome (SARS) crisis of 2003—and nothing had changed. The
SARS crisis, with its need for quarantine, would stress any health
care delivery system. It proved especially trying for Ontario's,
which having lost 12,000 hospital beds in the 1990s, was
stretched thin before the first patient appeared in March.[a] The
three hospitals comprising the University Health Network
cancelled 1,050 surgical procedures, including cancer and heart
surgeries and transplants.[b] The hospitals postponed 31,000
clinical visits.[c] Predictably, Canadians traveled to the United
States for MRIs and CT scans as well as urgent surgeries.[d] In the
SARS aftermath, hospitals found themselves battling budget
deficits and long waits for procedures. UHN, for example, targets
a maximum 28 day wait from referral to treatment for cancer
patients. "Prior to SARS we were at 62 days," UHN president
and CEO Tom Closson told the Medical Post. "We are now at
85 days and we think it's going to go to 100 days."[e]
(Sources: [a]Today's Choices... Tomorrow's Care: Key Facts
and Figures, Media Backgrounder, Ontario Hospital
Association, June 20, 2003, p. 3.
[b]Theresa Boyle, "Ontario Hospitals in 'New Normal'
Mode," Toronto Star, May 19, 2003, p. A-1.
[c]Andrew Skelly, "Promised $25M Won't Cover Backlog:
Catching Up On Surgeries Requires Much More Money,"
Medical Post, May 6, 2003.
[d]Tom Blackwell, "Hospital Closures Send Patients South
of Border: SARS Delays Treatments: Buffalo Diagnostic
Clinics Bustling with Canadian Customers," National Post,
April 10, 2003, p. A-16.
[e]Skelly, "Promised $25M Won't Cover Backlog," May 6, 2003.)

Long a source of national pride, Canada's heath care system is rapidly becoming a source of national anxiety. A public opinion poll conducted in July, 2004, found that more than eight in 10 Ontarians are concerned about waiting for diagnostic procedures, specialists, and surgery.ᵃ Another poll conducted in May 2004 found that 87 percent of Canada's business leaders would support seeking health care outside the government system if they had a pressing medical concern.ᵇ

(Sources: ᵃ"Doctors to Canada's Premiers: Future of Health Care Relies on Unity; New Provincial Poll Shows Declining Confidence in Health Care," Canada NewsWire, July 28, 2004. ᵇRobert Thompson, "Health Care a Growing Issue: Most would Support Using Private Care Rather than Waiting," Financial Post, May 17, 2004.)

In March 2004, a class-action lawsuit was launched against 12 Quebec hospitals on behalf of 10,000 patients who waited more than eight weeks for radiotherapy after being diagnosed with breast cancer. The woman who initiated the lawsuit had waited three months in vain for radiotherapy under Canada's public health care system before spending $10,000 to receive the costly treatment outside the country. The suit, the first of its kind, could entail damages as great as $37 million and have repercussions across Canada.[32]

On June 24, in one of the many e-mails I have received in response to my newspaper articles, a resident of Ontario provided me with these stories:

• My father was told by his ophthalmologist that he would not be able to schedule an appointment for a needed cataract operation until the hospital administrator gave the doctor his next annual package of operating time at the end of the month. What if there isn't enough money for my father's operation? Of course, we told him to go to Syracuse, NY, to pay for it and get it out of the way.

• My aunts and uncles living in the St. John, New Brunswick area tell me it's next to impossible to find a doctor if you don't already have one. None are taking new patients. It's pretty much the same case here in the Kingston, Ontario area. The politicians are considering licensing immigrants who have a medical education, in order to provide more physicians. One might think this will further reduce the standard of medical care in this country.

Stories such as these are common, and there are many more extreme examples. Eighteen-year-old Joshua Fleuelling experienced the dangers of the system in January 1999, when his ambulance was turned back from a Toronto emergency room. He was suffering from asthma, and by the time he reached the doors of the next closest emergency room, he was brain dead from lack of oxygen.[33]

Fifty-three-year-old Jan Norwood confronted the limits in the fall of 2000, when her doctor determined she needed her left hip replaced. She won't cost the government any money for 16 months, because she'll be languishing on a waiting list of more than 150 people in need of similar surgery. But the wait will cost *her* dearly—emotionally, physically, and financially. "My life and that of my family is severely impacted by my pain," Norwood wrote to then Ontario Health Minister Elizabeth Witmer. "I sleep less, am tired all the time, and my income (as a consultant) is significantly reduced. My client base is eroding. My costs are increasing and my drugs are expensive. The pain is unrelenting," continued Norwood, "it saps my energy and ruins my life."[34]

The system relies on global budgets to control costs. It is beyond dispute that one of the best ways to keep government budget expenses down in any given year is to choose not to invest in the latest equipment.

There's no question that Canada suffers from a shortage of new medical technology that can assist in diagnosis and treatments. This is fine from the administrator's perspective. But it's understandable that patients see it from a different angle—from the angle offered at the back of a long line.

Ottawa nurse Trish Besner had exactly that view in early 2001. The 31-year-old mother started experiencing fainting spells and was told in October 2000 that she needed an MRI to diagnose her condition. "The doctors keep mentioning MS to me," Mrs. Besner told the *Ottawa Citizen*. "That's a very scary thing and I know that an MRI can rule that out." Unfortunately, Ottawa has only one MRI for 555,000 residents, and more than 7,000 were already lined up for screening.

Many, like Canadian Senator Edward M. Lawson, cross over the border and pay for prompt care in the United States. Lawson experienced chest pains in August 2001 and his doctor told him he'd have to wait a month for an angiogram, the recommended diagnostic. No thanks, he said, as he headed to Seattle to purchase prompt care.
(Source: Crossette, "Canada's Health Care Shows Strains," 2001.)

So while the government saved on the $3.5 million price tag of an MRI machine, and the $2 million a year it takes to keep it running, Besner and her family bore many costs. All her doctor was able to do was offer a raft of drugs, one pill for her anxiety, another for her sleeping problems, and yet another for her seizures. They didn't work, which left her unable to care for her toddler. Her mother took an unpaid leave from her job to take care of her family. "She's lost weight. She's thin and drawn," says her mother. "But we have no information as to what is wrong with Trish."[35]

Tom Holland, director of diagnostic imaging for the Ottawa Hospital and, therefore, the man who grants access to the MRI, can only offer his sympathies. "Unfortunately, we hear these stories all the time," says Holland. "There's a tremendous amount of anxiety for the patients and a tremendous amount of anxiety for those who are working here as well. Everybody associated with this operation deals with this on a daily basis."[36]

Thus, health care in Canada is a DMV (Department of Motor Vehicles) experience—"take a number and wait in line." Jan Norwood, described above, faced nearly a year and a half of pain and lost income. Yet, presumably to control costs, her surgeon's time at the hospital had actually been cut by one-third.[37] Patients in such straits face stark choices.

When lines get too long, the provinces may actually pay for travel and treatment in the United States. Ontario, for example, sent just under 1,800 cancer patients to the US for care between April 1999 and May 2000. This diversion costs, on average, $20,000 per patient.[38] In December 2001, a court ruled that Ontario had to pay $150,000 to send a drug-addicted teen to the United States for treatment, since the wait for the 10 available beds was too long.[39]

These experiences would seem to violate the accessibility principle from the sacrosanct 1984 Canada Health Act, which states that provinces must provide "reasonable access" to care. But it turns out that the Act doesn't provide enforceable rights, at least when it comes to waiting in line. A study published in the *Canadian Medical Association Journal* finds that half of cancer patients wait more than 37 days for referral to surgery in Ontario's regional cancer centers.[40] The Canadian Society of Surgical Oncology recommends that patients receive surgery within two weeks.

When former Quebec premier Robert Bourassa discovered that he had skin cancer, he went to the United States and paid for his treatment there.

(Source: James Frogue, A High Price for Patients: An Update on Health Care in Britain and Canada, Backgrounder No. 1398, The Heritage Foundation (September 26, 2000).)

The Vancouver-based Fraser Institute has long been tracking waiting times in Canada through its annual surveys of doctors. Between 1993 and 2003, the median waiting time from referral by a general practitioner to treatment increased by 90 percent, from 9.3 weeks to 17.7 weeks. Waiting times increased across all specialties. For cancer patients, the waiting time for medical oncology more than doubled from 2.5 weeks to 6.1 weeks, and the waiting time for radiation oncology increased from 5.3 weeks to 8.1 weeks. Across all 10 provinces, waiting times increased.[41]

How you feel about this depends on whether you are a needy patient like Norwood and Lawson, or whether you are healthy, and ideologically and emotionally wedded to the current, top-down, single-payer plan. "Canadians do not wait for care that is required immediately," assert Pat and Hugh Armstrong, who claim that emergency rooms are available for everyone—a claim that didn't hold on January 2, 2000, when 23 of Toronto's 25 emergency rooms were closed to all.[42]

And the Armstrongs are not worried about quality of life. "While waiting for knee surgery might be inconvenient or even painful, it is unlikely to be life threatening." They also claim that in some cases waiting lines are "indications of the system's success, not its failure," since it shows strong demand for quality care.[43] In short, we are told there is reason to celebrate long lines. Policymakers advise patients to keep stiff upper-lips; and many of them do, as their lips curl from agony.

Of course, rationing by waiting is the inescapable product of a government-controlled system that funds hospitals with global budgets and doesn't allow the private purchase of services. "If the costs of hospitals and physicians are controlled, there will be continuing complaints about longer hospital waiting lists and the absence of the latest technology," writes Jane Fulton.[44]

As Fulton so candidly indicates, much of the waiting for care in Canada is, in fact, waiting for technology. This, too, is a product of the single-payer system of funding. And like the waiting lines that system produces, the intent in delaying technological improvement is to shift costs from the system, which would be born in the form of monetary costs, to needy patients, who pay in pain and suffering, as well as money. The more tightly the government tries to manage the system, the worse it gets.

"Does it make any sense that your cat can get an MRI at 2:30 in the morning and you can pay $20 to do that but your mother can't?" asked Ernie Eves, a candidate for premier of Ontario in January 2002. "Is your cat more important than your mother?"[45] Eves refers to the 1998 discovery by the *Toronto Star* that St. Joseph's Health Centre in London, Ontario, was renting access to its MRI machine to veterinarians for after-hours use while Canadian patients waited for diagnosis.[46]

It makes perfect sense, once you understand the incentives of the system. Canadian humans pay nothing for the services they receive. As a result, providing them with expensive services costs hospitals and provinces money. Pet owners, however, pay for the services their pets receive. Therefore, hospitals make money by providing them with extra services in the off hours—hours that transform equipment from being cost centers to revenue centers.

The same is true of foreigners, who travel to Canada for the fine care some of its specialized centers offer. In 1999, a member of the Moroccan royal family jumped ahead of hundreds of waiting Canadians to get heart surgery at a Montreal hospital. His $60,000 provided a windfall for the hospital, which claims to have opened up a closed bed for the procedure.[47]

Yet when Canadians want to spend $4 for x-rays—less than the cost of a Big Mac super-meal at McDonald's—the government won't allow it.[48] Waiting is the price they pay for free care.

There's no denying that Canada suffers from a lack of high-tech equipment, not just compared to the United States, but compared to all advanced countries.

According to the Organization for Economic Cooperation and Development (OECD), Canada had only 3.5 magnetic resonance imaging (MRI) units per million population in 2001. This compares to an average of 6.3 MRIs per million for the 25 OECD countries for which data were available. In fact, Canada ranked 16th out of 25 OECD countries in MRIs per capita.

The news is even worse for computed tomography (CT) scanners. Canada has only 9.5 CT scanners per million population, compared to an average of 16.7 CT scanners for the 24 OECD countries that make their data available. Among these 24 OECD countries, Canada ranked 20th in the number of CT scanners per capita.[49]

Even the equipment hospitals have is increasingly obsolete. The Canadian Association of Radiologists (CAR) reports that one in two diagnostic imaging units—ultrasound, x-ray, and CT scan machines—requires immediate replacement. One CT scan machine in a Montreal suburb can't even be turned off, CAR says, because it's so outdated that replacement parts, including the power switch, are no longer made.[50]

"Our radiology equipment is in bad shape," according to CAR CEO Normand Laberge, who pegs the national replacement cost at $2 billion. Without immediate action radiologists will no longer be able to guarantee the reliability and quality of examinations."

Old machines aren't replaced and new machines, even ones that greatly improve care, are not added. Canada has only two Positron Emission Tomography machines, or PET scanners, a relatively new diagnostic machine that employs radioactive chemicals to view molecular changes in cells and detect cancer. PET scans have proven extremely useful in detecting and diagnosing many types of cancer, including breast cancer.

A recent study found that PET scans caused doctors to change their treatment in six out of 10 cases, due to their greater precision.

"For patients with breast cancer, there really is the opportunity of being able to say, 'Look, we know your cancer treatment now isn't working,'" says Dr. Sandy McEwan, an Edmonton-based oncologist. "Because there are so many therapies for breast cancer, it is very important that we know exactly where we are managing patients. What is the cancer? Where is it? How is it responding? Because if we get it at the beginning of a failure of response we can change to treatments that we know work very well."[51]

Yet at a cost of up to $3 million a machine, Canadian provinces haven't eagerly purchased them. McEwan has access to a third machine, purchased with research money, which she's allowed to use only a few hours a week for patients.

A PET scanner "definitely changes the way we manage patients, avoiding lots of unnecessary surgery," says Dr. Francois Bénard, who has access to one of the fully operational scanners. "It helps us predict disease when other tests are negative. It saves a lot of pain and suffering for cancer patients."[52]

That's certainly the case—and it's why there are more than 250 PET scanners in the United States, 48 in Japan, 45 in Germany, and nearly 20 in Belgium. But although they help patients, these scanners provide pain and suffering to the budgets of health care planners.

"In Canada, hospitals are not free to develop services such as open-heart surgery and transplantation, or to purchase expensive equipment such as magnetic resonance imagining (MRI) scanners, without specific approval from provincial governments," explain an approving Rachlis and Kushner.[53] And when it comes to purchasing new PET scanners or replacing old x-ray machines, the governments simply say no.

"The large and growing gap between the United States and Canada," writes Canada's most vocal economist R.G. Evans and others in the *New England Journal of Medicine*, "drives home the point that, for good or ill, the form of funding adopted by Canada does permit a society to control its overall outlays on health care. Furthermore it is unnecessary to impose financial barriers to access in the process."[54]

Evans and associates penned these words in 1989, when Canada was spending 8.6 percent of its GDP on health care, the third highest percentage in the world. The claim was a stretch then. By 1993, the median wait time between referral by a general practitioner and treatment was 9.3 weeks. Today, it's clear that Evans's last sentence needs to be radically edited to state, "But it is necessary to impose significant non-financial barriers to access in the process."

In a private system, costs are not systemic issues, but are instead issues between buyers and sellers. Buyers, ideally individuals, but often large third parties such as employers or health plans, want to spend as little as possible to secure quality care. They must account for the non-monetary costs as well as the cash expenditures. Doctors, clinics, and hospitals want to sell their services for as high a price as possible. Individual negotiations, in which monetary and non-monetary costs are taken into account, produce the outcome.

Under a private system, doctors and hospitals view patients as beneficial, at least from the institutional perspective. Expecting mothers, seniors in need of joint replacements, and heart patients, are all welcomed and served, because they help sustain hospitals with their payments.

Under a system of global budgets, where hospitals are given a lump of money per year that's only loosely tied to individual procedures, patients are a pain in the budget for hospitals.

Surgery centers are cost, not revenue, centers for these hospitals. The only way to limit expenditures is to limit procedures by refusing to invest in expensive equipment and limiting surgeons' access to operating rooms. This is how costs are shifted to patients.

"For cardiac patients in Canada, because of the way health care is funded, you are looked at as a cost-center, someone who costs the provincial government a lot of money because what I do is expensive, technology driven, a lot of cost per life saved," Dr. Kevin Landolfo, a Canadian heart-transplant surgeon who transplanted himself to the Duke Medical Center in the United States, told Canadian author Jeffrey Simpson. "In the United States, it's seen as the exact opposite."[55]

Dr. Alfons Pomp, a Canadian laparoscopic surgeon who does his operating in the US, makes the same point. "There's no comparison because the basic difference is that in medical care in the United States, the more patients you operate on the better you

---

In December 2001, the press broke the story that health care bureaucrats in Queens Park instructed the Queensway-Carleton Hospital in Ottawa to ration babies. The facility is set to deliver 2,700 bundles of joy a year, but that's expensive under a system in which deliveries are "free."
So the bureaucrats set the hospital's quota at 2,100 newborns, and forced the hospital's delivery doctors to sign a contract that promised they would not exceed the quota. If they served too many parents, they would lose their jobs. "They figured they'd save $600,000," says Dr. Paul Legault, the hospital's chief of obstetrics, who fought the quota and got it raised to 2,500. "We felt we were being kicked out, penalized for providing service, which I thought was our job. I trained 12 years in order to do obstetrical care, not to sit in my office and refuse patients." (Source: Quoted in Margaret Wente, "How to Cut Health Care Costs: Ration Babies," Globe and Mail, December 13, 2001.)

are," Dr. Pomp tells Simpson. "You bring money in. The patient is a source of revenue. Whereas in Canada, the patient is a source of expense. So it's to the hospital's benefit to reduce costs (by) doing the least amount of operations as possible, as paradoxical as that seems."[56]

Hospitals must control their costs, so rationing of procedures is built into the system, year in and year out. Pomp notes that the average surgeon in Quebec performs only one operation a week, on a good week. Says Pomp, "When you have a waiting list and you're doing only one patient in every week, and you add three or four patients a week to the waiting list, it's obviously an untenable situation." [57]

Year after year, this incentive structure produces hospitals and surgery centers that are woefully inadequate at serving people. The rationing is often subtle, known to only the surgeons, who cannot obtain operating rooms or the latest technology, and their would-be patients. Sometimes absurd cases bring the situation to the public's attention. That is, of course, the case when it was discovered in 1998 that pets could get MRIs while their owners couldn't. It is also the case in the maternity ward, where each birth is a newborn cost center.

"I have witnessed health ministry employees argue that women with incontinence should not have access to collagen injections because 'they are only peeing themselves,'" writes Tim Lynch, who, as a health services reimbursement consultant, deals with health bureaucrats day in and day out. "Medication to inhibit vomiting in cancer patients, a side effect of chemotherapy, was greeted with the argument, 'they are only throwing up.'"
(*Source: Tim Lynch, "Choice in Health Care,"* Globe and Mail, *November 12, 2001.)*

"I had a nurse with me the entire time I was in labor and the doctor was always nearby," says Jane Don, thirty-three-year-old mother of two from Burlington, Ontario, who had her first child in 1993. Yet when she had her second three years later, personal care had turned into a group experience. She had to share two nurses and one doctor with five other women. She didn't get much attention, and believes she picked up an infection as a result.[58]

As Don's experience shows, the way bureaucrats save money is by shifting costs to patients. Consider the statement of health-care activists Pat and Hugh Armstrong: "While waiting for knee surgery might be inconvenient or even painful, it is unlikely to be life threatening." It's true that Jane Don's lack of attention didn't threaten her life; it just left her uncomfortable and perhaps caused a secondary infection, which also inconvenienced her and cost money to treat.

But is the goal of health care to intervene only when something is life threatening? Certainly, considerations such as comfort and peace of mind matter to patients. But when it comes time to budget, the Armstrongs' view rules the day.

Lynch points to exceedingly callous statements that, while jolting in their starkness, point to the calculations that take place in every aspect of the system's budgeting process.

Consider laparoscopic surgery. Unlike traditional surgery, it requires only small incisions, through which highly skilled surgeons use cameras and precision tools to perform procedures inside the body. It's less painful for patients and it reduces recovery times. The equipment, however, is expensive and, therefore, not prevalent in Canada.

"It's really a matter of having the tools to do my job," Emma Patterson, a native of British Columbia, told Simpson. Patterson was trained at Mount Sinai Hospital in New York by two other Canadian surgeons who were driven south by lack of resources and planned to return to Canada to practice her trade. The hospital at which she used to work in British Columbia just couldn't come up with the money to purchase the equipment she needed, so she planned to stay in the United States.[59] This is not an aberration, it's part of the system's design.

CHAPTER SIX:
How Does Canadian Federalism Work in Practice?

Political philosophers and scientists have long recognized that one of the major benefits of federalism—the division of government powers and responsibilities in different layers of government—is the diversity in approach to public policy issues that it allows. As markets cater to individual choices—ketchup lovers and salsa enthusiasts have no reason to quarrel, as they can each purchase their product of choice—a dispersion of governing regimes allows people a degree of freedom to choose the set of rules under which they live.

Federalism also promotes progress in public policy. As in other areas of life, improvements in public policy result from a relentless process of experimental trial and error, under which sound policies are retained and less beneficial policies either adjusted or jettisoned. As US Supreme Court Justice Louis Brandeis famously characterized, the states are "laboratories," from which sprung the popular phrase "laboratories of democracy."

The same is true in Canada. Indeed, it was through the mechanisms of federalism that single-payer health care became the norm in Canada. Over time, however, power was consolidated in Ottawa, culminating in the 1984 Canada Health Act placing uniform conditions on the provincial plans. The provinces should be set free to undertake bold experiments again.

The federal government had better listen. There are signs of restlessness and even outright rebellion in the provinces. In Alberta, Bill 11 allows private clinics to perform surgical procedures requiring overnight stays. This has prompted a backlash, with officials citing the Canada Health Act and threatening sanctions. Christine Burdett, chair of the Friends of Medicare lobby, asked how the public hospitals would save money if they keep paying the same overhead and staff costs as more surgery is contracted out. "Will we be paying the money twice?" she asked.

Nevertheless, some provinces may go ahead. Depending on which reforms the provinces are willing to push, they may want to confront Ottawa, violate the supreme health care law of the land, and accept the consequences. The reason: they may soon have no other choice.

In 2000, economist Martin Zelder calculated the net effects for the provinces if they were to violate the Canada Health Act's accessibility mandate by instituting a 25 percent co-insurance payment. An exhaustive study by the RAND Corporation found that such a co-insurance reduces health care use, but doesn't have a negative impact on the health of most participants.[60] Zelder estimates that this policy alone would save each province 19 percent of its current health care expenditure.

He then calculated the net effect to each province, which must account for the provincial money saved, as well as the loss of federal funding. It turns out that Alberta and Ontario would be better off going it alone under such an arrangement. Alberta could expect an $83 million windfall from opting out, while Ontario could expect a boost of $51 million.[61]

"A province intent on reforming its health care system can do so, if it is willing to pay the price in forgone (federal) transfers, and potential political opprobrium," notes Zelder. "Some may call that a sin, but in time when the current heath system forsakes so many who are suffering, it might instead prove the most saintly compassion."[62]

CHAPTER SEVEN:
How does the Canadian System Treat Pharmaceuticals?

In the United States, liberal politicians and advocates of nationalized health care have found something else in Canada's health care system to admire: its prescription drug policy. At least one politician, Michigan Democrat Debbie Stabenow, found that her trip to the US Senate in 2000 ran through Canada, where she staged many publicized bus trips for needy seniors.

"We have an industry that is the most profitable in the world," Stabenow told the *New York Times*. "And I don't begrudge them that in any way. But when an industry is allowed to make 18 to 20 percent a year, at the same time it's raising prices three times the rate of inflation, and people who need life-saving medicine cannot afford it, I think it's time to ask where the corporate responsibility is."[63]

The affection US liberals have for the Canadian system is ironic, because pharmaceuticals in Canada are explicitly excluded from the national health care mandate. The reason? As incredible as it sounds, the Canadian federal government does not consider pharmaceuticals to be medically necessary, at least not yet. The Canada Health Act does not require prescription drug coverage under the medicare system.

At the same time, Canadian provinces pay for nearly half of prescription drug expenses. In 2001, governments paid for 49 percent of prescription costs, private insurance paid for 30 percent, and individual out-of-pocket costs covered the remaining 21 percent.[64] Each province provides coverage for low-income elderly Canadians. Six in 10 Canadians enjoy some third-party coverage for prescription drugs.[65]

Canada also enforces strict price controls on what manufacturers can charge for patented drugs. Many drugs are less expensive in Canada than in the United States for this reason. Canada's national government also tightly regulates the drug industry, including the prices at which it can sell to distributors, the so-called "gate price" of the products. At first glance, this policy appears to have kept prices lower in Canada. But closer examination calls that into question. University of Pennsylvania professor Patricia Danzon found that US consumers would have paid three percent more in 1992 if they purchased the same bundle of drugs in Canada as they did in the United States.[66]

The governing law is the amended 1987 Patent Act, which established the Patented Medicine Prices Review Board (PMPRB). The PMPRB, which reports to Parliament, is charged with ensuring that prices for drugs are not excessive. This board places drugs into one of three categories, which determine acceptable prices.

Category One: New drugs that are extensions of existing medicines or of comparable dosage to existing medicines. A new drug placed in Category One cannot increase the cost of drug treatment for a disease. (The bureaucrats do not take into consideration any cost reductions in non-drug treatments when setting the prices.)

Category Two: A new drug that is the first to treat an illness, or is a substantial improvement over what's already available, is considered a breakthrough drug, and thus earns a coveted spot in this second category. The price of these Category Two drugs cannot be set so high that a bureaucrat deems it would increase the costs of treatment in its therapeutic class. Thus, breakthrough drugs are limited to the median price of the same drug in France, Germany, Italy, Sweden, Switzerland, Britain, and the United States.

Category Three: Reserved for what are derisively referred to as "me too" drugs. They are usually a new dosage or form of an existing drug. As such, the government doesn't consider them to add much improvement over what's already available. These drugs, like those in category one, can't increase the costs of therapy.

The Canadian Patented Medicine Prices Review Board rarely finds a drug to be a breakthrough drug. Between 1988 and 1995, the government only classified 41 out of 581 drugs as breakthrough. (Source: Menon, "Pharmaceutical Cost Control in Canada: Does It Work?" p. 99.)

Government meddling isn't limited to simply setting prices. The board also keeps track of every prescription that's sold. Companies are required to file detailed price and sales reports for every six-month period.[67] If government officials determine that companies are selling too much product at too high a price, they will demand that companies enter into a Voluntary Compliance Undertaking, an Orwellian euphemism, that results in industry givebacks to government and even fines.[68]

In 1998, the price of Eli Lilly's insulin drug, Humalog, was reduced from $30 to $23 as part of a Voluntary Compliance Undertaking. Eli Lilly paid the Canadian government $666,824 as part of the Undertaking to offset the "excess revenues" it had previously earned.[69]

Provinces aren't content to leave regulation to the federal government. They also regulate pharmaceuticals. "Formularies" are the primary means by which they regulate. Pharmaceuticals first must be approved by the federal government, which, as mentioned, classifies them and assigns an acceptable price range. They must then be approved by provincial governments, which include them in their formularies of approved drugs.

Again, one might expect such approval to be a formality, since one set of government officials has already given the product a thumbs-up. At the very least, since the process should be objective, one would expect drug approvals not to vary except in rare cases across the provinces. Neither assumption is true.

Often a drug will be approved for inclusion in some provincial formularies, but find itself shut out of others. Of 23 cardiovascular drugs approved by the national government between 1991 and 1998, one province covered only 10, while another covered 22.[70] The federal government approved 99 new drugs in 1998 and 1999. Yet the Ontario formulary included only 25.[71]

The reason is no mystery. Delay saves money. Ontario takes nearly 500 days to approve a drug while Nova Scotia gets the job done in half the time.[72]

This, of course, hurts patients, for whom the drug might provide added benefit. It makes a mockery of the idea that the process is based on objective science. It also conflicts with the notion that all Canadians have equal access to health care, as ensured by the Canada Health Act. But as mentioned, pharmaceuticals aren't considered medically necessary and, therefore, aren't covered by the act.

Other methods some provinces use to limit patients' access to the full range of pharmaceutical products include "generic substitution" and "reference-based pricing."

Under generic substitution, provinces require that when drugs are available from more than one source, a generic version be used.

Under reference-based pricing, government officials create therapeutic categories, each with two or more drugs that can be used to treat the category's illness.

The reference product is the one with the lowest price. Provinces will only reimburse patients for this price, regardless of which drug is actually suitable for the patient's individual condition. Under reference-based pricing, different drugs are placed in the same category for treatment of an ailment. The cheapest drug might not be the most effective one for many patients. That doesn't matter to the government.

It often does matter, however, to patients who are forced to change medication when the government decides to shift its products, which it often does. Some 27 percent of physicians in British Columbia have had to admit patients to the emergency room or admit them to the hospital due to the adverse effects of a switch in medication.[73]

While in private practice, the former chief coroner of British Columbia, Dr. William McArthur, was forced to admit a 64-year-old patient to the hospital after the government switched that patient to an older, cheaper, and less effective drug to treat his peptic ulcers. It only took three days on the cheaper drug to cause enough bleeding for him to require a lifesaving blood transfusion. This is a classic example of the system shifting costs to both patients and the larger health-care system.
(Source: McArthur, "Prescription Drug Costs: Has Canada Found the Answer?" May 19, 2000.)

Reference pricing distorts consumer behavior, which in turn defeats the effort to cut costs.

Worst of all, reference-based pricing flunks at its primary task—controlling costs. Prior to the enactment of British Columbia's Reference Drug Program in 1995, both public and private drug spending grew at a slower pace in British Columbia than in other Canadian provinces.

Since enactment of the RDP in 1995, both public and private drug spending in British Columbia have grown faster than other provinces.[74]

At the same time, reference pricing may lead to the purchase of an inferior drug for treating an illness. British Columbia does grant "special authority" for patients who demonstrate the need for an expensive drug in one of the therapeutic clusters. When a patient is granted special authority, the province will pay for the full cost of a high-priced drug within a cluster (not including the dispensing fee).

This may be one reason why British Columbia has seen drug spending rise faster since the introduction of the Reference Drug Program. The province continues to provide nearly full drug coverage for many patients, and it is unclear to what extent the "special authority" provision may be subject to abuse.

The emerging field of behavioral economics has shown that reference-based pricing strongly influences consumer behavior. In an experiment, subjects were told that they could purchase a calculator for $15 or travel 20 minutes to purchase the same calculator at another store for $10. Sixty-eight percent of respondents said they would make the trip to save the five dollars.

However, when the price of the calculator was put at $125 and consumers were told they could travel 20 minutes to buy it at another store for $120, only 29 percent said they would travel to save the five dollars.[a] In both cases the identical trip would save five dollars, but consumers were much more willing to seek out the five-dollar savings when nominal prices were lower.

This counterintuitive finding upsets the standard theory of economic behavior, which holds that a rational, self-interested consumer will be consistent in weighing benefits and costs. "Prospect theory," as developed by Nobel laureate Daniel Kahneman and the late Amos Tversky, recognizes that consumers assign value to total costs, rather than the price differences themselves.

In effect, individuals place greater value on the first dollar than on the second, place a greater value on the second dollar than the third, and so on. Thus, for many consumers, the difference between $5 and $10 looms larger than the difference between $120 and $125.

(Source: [a]Daniel Kahneman and Amos Tversky, "Choices, Values, and Frames," in Daniel Kahneman and Amos Tversky, eds., Choices, Values, and Frames (New York: Cambridge University Press, 2000): 11-12.)

Another reason for increasing drug spending in British Columbia is the high prices for generic drugs. A study looking at the lowest prices available for 27 generic drugs in the US and Canada found that 21 drugs had lower prices in the United States.[75] On average, the Canadian generics cost 37 percent more.

Health policy experts believe this results from a lack of competition in the generics market in Canada. Because the Patented Medicine Prices Review Board sets price controls on brand-name drugs, there is less of a discount when generics are brought to market. As a result, two firms dominate the Canadian generics industry.[76]

In British Columbia, reference pricing may also contribute to inflated generic drug prices. Since the ingredient cost of the reference drug is fully subsidized under the RDP, there is no incentive for generic drug makers to hold down prices. And unlike brand-name drugs, the PMPRB does not set maximum prices for generics.

Other provinces, however, have enacted their own price controls on generics. Ontario requires that the first generic drug be priced 30 percent less than the brand-name drug and that subsequent generic competitors be priced even lower.[77] Quebec requires generic drug makers to offer the "best price" they offer anywhere else in Canada.[78] But with Quebec being the second most populous province, this provides a disincentive for generic drug makers to offer lower prices in other provinces.

Price competition is the reason why most generics are less expensive in the United States. Some famous cost comparisons, including Senator Hillary Clinton's comparison of the price of the allergy medication Claritin in Canada and the United States, are simply inaccurate. Activists cite US drug prices and Canadian drug prices as if there's a single price in each country. This is fiction. The prices for the same product vary from area to area and store to store in both countries. There's no such thing as a US price and a Canadian price.[79]

Nevertheless, retail prices are lower in Canada for some high-profile, brand-name drugs, as Americans going north of the border can attest. If prices on the drugs they were purchasing weren't lower, Americans most certainly wouldn't spend the $100 for the round trip and waste a day on travel. Still, there are reasons other than government price controls that explain lower retail prices in Canada.

One reason drug prices are lower in Canada is that the general price level is lower in Canada. Countries with lower per-capita earnings have prices for the same product that are lower than in countries with higher earnings per-capita. As hard as it is for Canadians to think of themselves as poorer than their southern neighbors, the fact is that they are, and in relative terms they are getting poorer.

In 1987, drug prices were only six percent lower in Canada. By 1998 the gap had widened to 25 percent.[80]

In 2000, AOL, for example, cost $21.95 per month in the United States, but only US $16 in Canada. Intuit's personal finance software program, Quicken Basic 2000, cost $34.95 in the United States, but only US $20 in Canada.[81]

There are other complications. Government regulations and the US legal system produce costs that aren't accounted for in simple cross-country price comparisons. In Canada, lawyers aren't allowed to sue their way to riches.

In the United States, it's not only allowed, but as current efforts by state attorneys general against the pharmaceutical industry show, it's actively encouraged by government officials. And some of the money finds its way back into the campaign coffers of politicians, who pass more laws encouraging more lawsuits. (As a group, lawyers are the largest contributors to the US Democratic Party.)[82]

A recent study found that lawsuits accounted for between one-third and one-half of the drug price differentials between the two countries.[83]

> *Canada has a significantly longer drug-approval process than the US. In 1995, the median time for drug approvals was 650 days in Canada, versus 464 days in the United States.*
>
> *(Source: Roy J. Romanow, Building on Values: The Future of Health Care in Canada, Commission on the Future of Health Care in Canada (November 2002), p. 201.)*

The Canadian pricing system also produces unintended consequences. The most obvious one is that by limiting Canadian access to drugs, it shifts costs onto patients. Due to excessive government regulation, pharmaceutical companies take much longer to launch products in the Canadian market than they do in the US market.

Even after products are launched, there can be significant lags before the products are approved for inclusion into provincial formularies. One hundred new drugs were launched in the United States from 1997 through 1999. Only 43 made it to market in Canada in that same period.[84]

Some drugs simply aren't available in Canada.[85] As late as 2002, Paxil Control Release, an advanced anti-depressant, still wasn't available in some parts of Canada and diabetes patients couldn't purchase Glucophage XR, a once-a-day treatment, anywhere north of the border.[86] It's not the bureaucrats who suffer the consequences, but Canadian patients.

Chapter Eight:
Still, Americans Are the Ones Taking Buses to Canada, Right?

The truth is, busloads of drug seekers go both ways. It's rarely reported in the United States, but Canadians head south by the busload to purchase pharmaceuticals that aren't available in their country at any price.[87]

In 2001, 12 percent of Canadian health care spending was for prescription drugs, compared to 10 percent in the United States.[88]

One reason for the difference is the higher prices for generic drugs charged in Canada. As mentioned in the previous section, 21 of 27 top-selling generic drugs cost more in Canada than in the United States.[89]

This can be explained largely by a lack of competition—two firms dominate the market for generic drugs in Canada. Canadian price controls only apply to patented prescription drugs, not generics. Patented drugs don't compete on price, even as older less effective drugs face competition from new drugs. Since the government sets the price for new drugs based on the price for existing drugs in the same class, drug companies are unwilling to cut the prices of existing drugs, because it would mean getting an even lower price on their new products.

Unlike in the United States, where manufacturers of older drugs and second- and third-choice patented drugs have an incentive to increase sales by lowering price, no such incentive exists in Canada. In fact, the opposite incentive exists. Because of price controls on brand-name drugs, generics provide a smaller discount in Canada and this discourages firms from offering competing products. The result is that manufacturers of generic drugs don't face stiff competition from older patented drugs and can, therefore, charge higher prices.[90]

Due to the large portion of the US drug market held by generics—roughly 50 percent—Americans would often spend more on drugs if they had to pay Canadian prices for all the drugs they consume, not just the latest patented drugs.

One final point on the Canadian system must be made. It is a free rider on the US system, which is to say that when Canadians pay lower prices for the latest patented drugs, it is because Americans are willing and able to pay higher prices for the same drugs.

As noted in the US section, the United States is the only place on earth where the incentives still exist to fund robust research in pharmaceutical progress. If the United States were to adopt the Canadian system or allow pharmacies to re-import Canadian drugs into the US market, the result in the former case would be fewer new drugs available in Canada.

In the latter case, Canadians would either end up paying the same prices that Americans pay or, if prices were to remain low in Canada, they would find that they were unable to purchase drugs because none would be available. Even more Canadians would be forced to board buses for the United States or visit US web sites. Either way, they'd pay US prices or go without pharmaceuticals.

Like the single-payer system, Canada doesn't offer a healthy pharmaceutical model for the United States—or anyone else—to follow.

CHAPTER NINE:
Is there a Role for the Private Sector in Canada?

At the beginning of 2002, private companies in Canada operated 19 MRI machines, seven CT scanners, and one PET scanner.[91] All these operations were constrained, and sometimes harassed, by government. Some, however, are actually contracted by the government to relieve stress from the public system. Cancer Care Ontario, for example, is contracting with Canadian Radiation Oncology Services, Ltd., to run an after-hours radiation clinic. Union activists have protested the contract. But until the contract was signed, Ontario was sending breast and prostate cancer patients to the United States for care at a cost of $20,000 each.[92]

The Calgary Regional Health Authority contracted with two organizations, Western Canada MRI Centre and Mayfair Diagnostics, to serve patients stuck on waiting lists from May 2000 to March 2001.[93]

Clinics that aren't operating under a government contract operate under the absurd stipulation that they can only provide non-medically necessary care. This means that people can purchase an MRI, for example, as part of some feel-good routine check up, similar to the body scans in the United States. But if their doctor orders it as part of a treatment program, they must queue up for the publicly purchased machines.

Frank Fedyk, Canada's director-general of intergovernmental affairs, told the *Globe and Mail* that if it is medically necessary the government should pay for it. Yet the federal government spends $4 million a year to ferret out and punish private clinics that violate the public administration requirement of the Canada Health Act.

CHAPTER TEN:
Are there Benefits to
the Canadian System?

In Canada, where half of households are wired to the Internet, 23 percent consult the web for health care information, a source second only to the family doctor.[94] Doctors frequently confront patients who have downloaded information about what they think ails them, such as studies from medical journals available on Medline or information from chat groups.

Telemedicine is an important innovation bringing benefits to Canada, a vast country, much of it sparsely populated. Accordingly, Canada's provinces support numerous telemedicine projects. A tele-homecare project in the Canadian province of New Brunswick links patients' homes to a cardiac center, so that patients can return home more quickly.[95] The most commonly reimbursed telemedicine services are dermatology, pediatrics, psychiatry, and radiology.[96]

Still, Canadian telemedicine hasn't yet lived up to its full promise; it lacks capital investment. In a market system, patients are seen as revenue sources and technology as a way to serve them better and, therefore, increase revenue. In a public system, as we have seen many times, spending on technology is seen as a cost to be avoided or at least carefully controlled. "From the government's perspective," notes a study on fee-for-service telemedicine reimbursements, "one of its major concerns is uncontrolled utilization that could drive up health care spending."[97]

That's why the Ontario Hospital Association notes that while Information and Communications Technology (ICT) increases efficiency, "the Ontario health care sector has consistently underinvested in ICT, compared to other health care sectors in leading industrialized countries and other sectors of the economy."[98] Little surprise, then, that the association's report called for an expanded role for the private sector in getting up to date with this technology.

Another positive aspect of the Canadian system is the greater freedom Canadian doctors enjoy than their colleagues to the south. Unlike US doctors, who are second-guessed by managed-care companies, Canadian doctors are free to treat their patients as they see fit. They are constrained not by proscriptive regulations, but by lack of resources.

"We live in a much smaller house, but we're free to move around in the house," says one doctor. "American physicians live in a mansion, but they are constrained from moving from room to room. Canadian physicians never have their individual judgment challenged on how to treat a patient. The decisions we make are constrained, because we don't have the resources to do what we want to do."[99]

This is tolerable to a point. There must, after all, be some limits on the amount of resources a society devotes to any one thing, including health care. And if the service is to appear free to the consumer, then providers must be restricted either actively by managers, or passively by global budgets. But it's getting to the point that some doctors are questioning single-payer's impact on quality.

Fewer than three in 10 doctors rated their access to advanced equipment as good or better in a 1998 survey conducted by the Canadian Medical Association.[100]

"The system in this country is close to the end of the line," Dr. Jean Roch Lafrance, a 31-year veteran of Canadian medicine wrote in January 2001. "Hospitals are overcrowded, waiting times are unacceptably long, services have to be bought from the United

States for cancer patients, doctors are overworked and demoralized, nurses are not given a fair shake, and the aging population is a looming problem."[101]

"It breaks my heart to see severely disabled patients in the office and have to tell them I can't operate on them for 14 months," Dr. Alan Giachino, chief of orthopedic surgery at the Ottawa Hospital, wrote to former Ontario Premier Mike Harris in late 2000. "Some people can't walk. They are living in pain."[102]

CHAPTER ELEVEN:
Are there Signs that Canada is Correcting its System?

More and more Canadians are coming to think outside the box. They are beginning to allow the private sector—that is, investors interested in a profit—to build and operate the necessary facilities. This appears to violate the Canada Health Act's first principle of public administration. It may require a change in federal public policy, but that change is inevitable.

In fact, it has already begun to happen. In Ontario, the Ministry of Health has had a wish list of $2.5 billion worth of capital projects. Tight budgets, however, have meant that the government has only been able to spend $200 million.[103] As a result, the government has entered into an agreement with a private firm. The firm will build and own the $350 million hospital in Brampton, Ontario, which should be completed in 2006. The government will lease the facility from the firm and operate the hospital.[104]

"I do believe that the private sector should be given the opportunity to show whether or not it has the expertise to build a new hospital for Brampton efficiently, quickly, and within budget," said then Ontario health minister Tony Clement in 2001.[105] Jim Flaherty, the province's finance minister, was enthusiastic about the project. Said Flaherty, "There's a win-win here where we can use private capital and still preserve our revenues within the province to help fund care on an annual basis."[106]

The private sector has already been proving itself in other areas. A private diagnostic clinic recently opened in Nova Scotia that allows its citizens to pay for such things as MRIs and bone-density tests. It has sparked opposition. "This is one more glaring example of how provinces violate the Canada Health Act," says Dr. Michael Rachlis, a Toronto-based health policy analyst. "People are supposed to receive equal access to medical services not predicated on finances. Nova Scotians (with money) who need MRIs will get faster service than those who cannot afford to pay."[107] But the project is pushing forward.

As we've seen, in Alberta the government—looking for ways to relieve the pressure on the public system—approved Bill 11. Alberta Premier Ralph Klein had watched his father suffer considerable pain while waiting for a hip replacement surgery. The political battle was bitter, with the national health minister campaigning against the law. But it passed. "Profit-driven medicine has arrived in Alberta big time," liberal health critic Kevin Taft told the *Globe and Mail*. "Three or four years from now, big pieces of Alberta's health care system will not be recognizable."[108] Taft was engaging in overstatement typical of medicare's defenders any time a marginal reform is proposed to make the system more responsive to consumers. Three years later, nothing much had changed. Unfortunately, that included the long queues for essential services.

Bill 11, which took effect in 2000, allows the use of privately owned, for-profit, stand-alone surgery centers for a limited number of operations. In April 2000, there were already 53 for-profit, private clinics performing day surgeries such as cataract removal, hernias, and cosmetic work.[109] The move was controversial, because the procedures, unlike those at the diagnostic clinics, were paid for with public insurance.

In February 2002, the province went even further, approving the use of for-profit clinics for procedures such as hip and knee replacements and lower back surgery that require overnight stays.[110] In one sense, the bill and its effects are quite modest; private contracts in Alberta account for only 0.15 percent of provincial health spending.

There's enough private activity that Canada's central government is concerned. Health Canada, the federal department that oversees the Canada Health Act, spent $600,000 studying the issue. "I'm not sure anybody has a handle on it," says Geoffrey Gurd, a Health Canada official.[111]

The non-medically necessary care that Vancouver-based International P.E.T. Diagnostics provides seems necessary to its clients. In its first 20 months in operation, it has served just under 800 patients who paid Can $2,500 to get a powerful diagnosis of their condition. The majority of patients are from British Columbia, but even without advertising it is attracting patients from as far away as Newfoundland.[112]

Increasingly, patients from the United States are traveling north to take advantage of the bargain price. Patients must have a referral from a doctor. Many have been diagnosed with cancer and want the powerful imaging to see how extensively the cancer has spread and whether surgery is a viable treatment option.

So far, this company is the first and only private clinic offering PET scans, although it is actively working with the government to get its services covered. It is also looking to expand into Montreal and Toronto. "We recognized that it was going to take some time before provincial governments could see their way to having PET scans in public facilities," executive vice-president John Smith told the *National Post*. "And there's not much point in having just one grocery store. You need a chain to really be successful and meet the needs of investors."[113]

International P.E.T. Diagnostics is a classic entrepreneurial venture striving to meet unmet needs. It was founded by an architect who had a personal experience—one that forced him to confront and deal with Canada's public under-investment in high-tech diagnostic equipment. He realized that if Canadians were going to have access to the technology, it would have to be the private sector that made it available. His effort has been low-profile; he has worked with government authorities and private insurance companies to get his company's scans covered. In the meantime, people are willing to pay out of pocket. "People will pay for it because it can save their lives," Normand Laberge, executive director of the Canadian Association of Radiologists, told the *National Post*.[114] "Where there's a need, people will find a way to get it."

The Canadian private sector continues to innovate. Since 1995, Canadian insurance companies have been selling a product called critical-illness insurance. Unlike health insurance that pays for medical bills, or life insurance that pays one's survivors a lump sum of money, critical-illness insurance, sold in bundles that range from $15,000 to $2 million, pays policy holders a lump sum of money if they are diagnosed with a serious disease. The idea is to enable people to pay for the treatment of the disease.

A Boston-based company, Best Doctors, is providing new alternatives for Canadian patients who have bought critical-illness insurance by putting very ill patients in contact with the best doctors internationally for their conditions, and making arrangements for their care. Best Doctors is now the product of two companies that merged in 2001. One of them, HRT Inc., was founded in 1989 by two Harvard doctors to arrange for and manage the care of critically ill patients in Latin America who couldn't afford to travel to the United States for care. HRT provided for second opinions by Harvard doctors and assisted patients in arranging care. It operated in many countries but not the United States.

Best Doctors, the other company in that merger, was founded by Pulitzer Prize-winning authors Greg White Smith and Steven Naifeh in 1992. Six years earlier, Smith had been diagnosed with a supposedly inoperable brain tumor and given two months to live. After tracking down specialists, Smith received the necessary operation. He co-founded Best Doctors to help other critically ill patients find the world's best treatment for their condition.

Today the merged company operates in 27 countries including the United States. It covers 10 million people and offers five services. These include a second opinion, assistance in locating the best doctor for a person's condition, linking patients up with the best hospitals, and managing the case of a patient—everything from plane tickets and hotel arrangements to schools for children who may need to relocate for an extended period of time. The fifth service, financing for the treatment, is offered in some countries but not in the United States.

In Canada, for example, financing for Best Doctors comes from the critical-illness insurance.

"In designing our products," says Gabriela Perez, Marketing and Communications Manager at Best Doctors, "we took into consideration the new health care consumer. Currently in Canada patients have tremendous problems with government insurance, which is a good system but has problems with waiting lines. You cannot wait for radiation for four months when it is suggested that you need treatment within four weeks."[115]

Best Doctors, which handles thousands of cases a year, is an example of the internationalization of health care and the growing demands of health care consumers. It seeks to serve the three dominant groups in the health care marketplace: patients, doctors, and payers.

Its fundamental product is the same for everyone—matching the best care with those who need it, and making the process as convenient as possible. Yet the specifics of its products and marketing depend on the policy environment in each country. So in Canada, for example, it's teamed up with Canada Life and four other critical care insurers.[116]

CHAPTER TWELVE:

What is the Prognosis for Canada if It Doesn't Reform?

If Canada fails to reform, which physician will be the last one to turn out the lights at the clinic?

Emma Patterson, the Canadian surgeon who transplanted herself to the US who we met in Chapter 5, represents a problem for Canada: many of the country's highly skilled and expensively trained doctors move to the United States.

Ross Finnie of Queen's University School of Policy Studies found that 18.7 Canadian physicians left for the United States for every physician that came to Canada from the United States.[117] Some 15.3 Canadian nurses left for the United States for every nurse that came to Canada from the United States.[118]

In some cases, this exodus is driven by money—American doctors earn more and face a lower tax burden than do Canadian doctors. But more often decisions are based on non-monetary factors. Emma, after all, would prefer to practice in British Columbia, but she can't count on the province paying for the equipment she needs to provide the level of care at which she's been trained.

"It's a big dilemma for me," she says of her decision to practice in Portland, Oregon. "It's really a matter of having the tools of my trade available, just to be able to do the job, the best job I can do."[119]

As a surgeon, her tools cost a bundle. She estimates it would cost her former hospital in Vancouver at least $500,000 to provide her with the tools of her trade. The chief of surgery was working on it, but he'd only been able to come up with $100,000.

The Canadian Medical Association (CMA) estimated in 1996 that almost one-half of medical school graduates in Canada departed the country before ever practicing medicine in Canada.[a] That is a dramatic increase from about one-third in 1991, and is in addition to the already-practicing physicians that departed the country or retired early.

(Source: [a]Victor Dirnfeld, "Canadian Physicians and the Brain Drain," CMA Submissions to Parliament, Canadian Medical Association, June 9, 1998.)

And even when health care bureaucrats give hospitals the green light to purchase high-tech equipment, there's the cost of running it. Recall that under global budgets, each operation costs hospitals money, and, therefore, less is better, from the perspectives of budgeters. That's what drove Dr. Michel Gagner to go south.

"We did not have enough operating time to take care of all these patients. We did not have any team to take care of patients after surgery or organize their preoperative care. So we decided it was time to move," said Gagner, who worked at Hôtel-Dieu and the Université de Montréal. "I had a two-year waiting list, if you can believe that. Every day, patients were calling me and saying, 'When, when, when?' I couldn't take the pressure anymore."[120]

Surveys show that doctors are losing faith in the ability of government bureaucrats to run the system.

According to a survey, two-thirds of doctors and nurses are losing confidence in the Canadian health care system, which they feel needs major reconstructive surgery.[121]

Dr. Jean Roch Lafrance, who's been practicing general medicine and anesthesia in Cornwall, Ontario, for more than 30 years, agrees. "The system in this country is close to the end of the line. Tweaking will not do," writes Lafrance. "There is a shortage of doctors. It's obvious. In our community, if we lose one of our two obstetricians (which is a distinct possibility), we will have to close our hospital's obstetrics ward. We are short one ophthalmologist, who moved to the United States. An orthopedist, a surgeon, and a urologist are also sought. In my 30-plus years in Cornwall I have seen dozens of physicians leave for the United States, with only a few returning. I have never seen a US-trained citizen come to town."[122]

A 2001 survey of 1,806 Canadian doctors found that 64 percent of doctors believe that health funds are misallocated, and three in four don't expect planners to improve the system in the next five years.
(Source: Tom Arnold, "MDs Show Little Faith in Health System," National Post Online, November 27, 2001.)

The Canadian Association of Radiologists (CAR) reports that six percent of Canadian radiologists are working without accreditation. The shortage is driven by two factors, according to CAR. First, governments have cut back funding for training by 10 percent, which means fewer graduates. Compounding the problem is the southern drift: CAR expects 25 percent of graduates to take fellowships outside of Canada.[123]

The College of Family Physicians of Canada reports that two-thirds of Canadian doctors are refusing new patients. "I went to 44 doctors before I finally got one," says Fay Sherlock of Burnaby, BC, who requires both physical and mental care. "Doctors don't want complex cases."[124]

And why should they? With government setting billing rates, the pay is the same for an easy versus a complicated visit, and the former takes less time.

By American standards, the financial control government wields over physicians is excessive. For example, the provinces of Ontario and Quebec reduce physicians' fees when their income exceeds a certain threshold.[125] Such measures make the appeal of practicing in the United States, where physicians earn far more money, self-evident.

The government also determines reimbursement rates and uses global budgets to allocate finite annual amounts of money to be used for doctors' payments for the entire year. This has not only led to low rates of payment, it has also resulted in doctors closing their offices and taking vacations.[126] Given these conditions, it is not surprising that many Canadian doctors are losing enthusiasm for the system.

It is estimated that Canada already needs about 2,500 new physicians per year to meet the nation's health care needs. That is about 500 new physicians per year more than the current supply.[127] Physician shortages will become more severe unless dramatic changes occur. According to Dr. June Bergman of the Calgary Regional Health Authority, Calgary, a city of about 850,000 residents, is 200 physicians short. With only 800 doctors, Calgary is attempting to recruit from overseas.[128]

CHAPTER THIRTEEN:

What is the Romanow Commission Report? How Will It Affect Access and Quality of Care?

The Canadian public's clamor for reform prompted the federal government to create a Commission on the Future of Health Care in Canada. Unfortunately, from a market reformer's point of view, the government appointed former socialist Saskatchewan Premier Roy Romanow to head the commission. By appointing Romanow the government made it clear that the "reforms" to be recommended by the commission would not involve market-based solutions.

In November 2002 the commission released its final report, *Building on Values: The Future of Health Care in Canada*. The sentiment of the report is expressed early on in such statements as, "Our health care system is adequately meeting our needs"[129] and "There is no 'invisible hand' that silently and unobtrusively keeps (services and resources) in place."[130]

The report recommends that the federal government spend an additional $9.7 billion over the following three years to pay for "more diagnostic services such as MRIs and CT scans, bring home care into the national system, strengthen primary care, and cover some drug costs for patients with catastrophic illness."[131]

In February 2003, Canadian political leaders agreed to transfer an additional $8 billion to the provinces over the next three years in order to provide catastrophic drug coverage and home care. Provinces immediately denounced the money as insufficient.[132] Provincial governments said the federal government would have to spend Can $50 billion over the next five years just to raise its share of funding to 25 percent from its anemic 14 percent.[133]

Like other Canadian policy elites, Romanow blames Canadians for expecting too much from their health care system: "Canadians are being influenced by what they see and hear on American television, which is usually high-tech medical breakthroughs and high public expectations."[134] Yet for all its complaining about state-of-the-art medicine and diagnostic services, the Romanow report recognizes that access to high-tech medicine can save money in reduced hospital costs.

"I go to Emergency when I am sick; there are no other choices," Canadian Ross Howard states in the report. "Waiting to see a specialist is a long-term wait; usually about 6-12 months."[135] In response, the report calls for the government to spend billions of dollars on a Diagnostic Services Fund. However, it rejects the idea that Canadians should be able to use their own money to purchase services from private facilities.[136] Nor does the report take into consideration how people help reduce costs in the public system when they use their own money to purchase care from private facilities instead of waiting to rely on taxpayer money.

The Romanow Commission also issued several recommendations regarding prescription drugs that would give the federal government new, top-down powers to impose its will. The federal government would finance a Catastrophic Drug Transfer to the provinces that would give Canadians protection against catastrophic drug expenses. This funding would give the federal government the cover it needs to create a new National Drug Agency (NDA) that would subsume regulatory powers from the provinces.

For instance, the NDA would implement a national drug formulary, something the provinces currently do. This is intended to make the availability of drugs uniform across the country. The report also justifies the creation of an NDA by saying pharmaceutical lobbying has influenced provinces in their choice of drugs for formularies. However, it is difficult to see why such lobbying would not influence decisions about the national formulary as well. This new agency and its national formulary are really initial steps toward the goal of bringing prescription drugs under the Canada Health Act.

The National Drug Agency would also subsume the price-control functions of the Patented Medicine Prices Review Board, with its authority expanded to include generic prescription drugs to "ensure that the price of all prescription drugs is fair to consumers."[137]

In addition, it envisions a more activist role for government toward the pharmaceutical industry:

> A National Drug Agency would combine the forces of the provinces, territories and the federal government and increase our ability to influence the policies of major pharmaceutical companies."[138]

Under the heading of be careful what you ask for, Canada's premiers accepted Romanow's offer and took it one step further. In August 2004, they presented a plan to have the federal government skip the go-slow approach and create a national pharmacare plan under medicare. The premiers neglected to put a price tag on their ambitious plan to shift pharmaceutical spending up a level of government. Interestingly, Romanow dismissed the proposal. "It's predicated on a whole number of concepts which I think need to be re-examined," said Romanow. "They haven't thought this through."[139] Regardless of whether Canadian policymakers follow Romanow's more modest, or the premiers' more ambitious approach, the problems will only worsen in the Canadian health care industry. Despite increased federal spending, the predictable result will be fewer doctors, less technology, and longer queues.

CHAPTER FOURTEEN:
What are the Solutions for Canada?

Canadians are proud of the health care system they've created. Unfortunately, due to the large role of government, it has failed to keep up with the times. As Dr. Robert Lifeso puts it, "Canada has some of the best medicine the 1970s can provide."[140]

This may be an assault on Canada's national identity, but it is one Canadians will soon have to deal with as the system continues to deteriorate. Canada's emotional attachment to its single-payer approach, enshrined in the five principles of the Canada Health Act, combined with the inaccurate view of how health care actually operates in the United States, severely limits the range of options considered by serious reformers.

Even so, the system's contradictions—the inefficiencies, inequalities, and high cost of providing government financed "free care"—are prompting some politicians to think the unthinkable and propose the unproposable: allowing more private sector involvement in the health care system, and moving toward a system where patients actually pay for a portion of the care they receive.

There are solutions, if Canadians are willing to break with the past, open the system to competition, and grant the consumer the power to make decisions. Such a break with the past would:

• Make the provincial insurance plans and the taxes that fund them voluntary.

- Open these plans to direct competition from private, non-profit, and for-profit insurers.
- Allow doctors to charge whatever they like and organize their practices in any way they choose.
- Permit private companies to build and operate the necessary capital-intensive facilities that Canada currently lacks and to do so at a profit.

Ultimately, what is needed is for the provincial monopoly of government-run insurance programs to be open to competition from private insurance.

This thinking is beginning to seep into official studies. A study of national medicare by the Standing Committee on Social Affairs, Science, and Technology, offered a slightly bolder vision for Canada than did the Romanow Commission. It recognized the deterioration of Canada's system and recommended that patients be allowed to flee the country when waiting lines get too long.[141] Still, it rejected internal reforms such as private insurance, user fees, and Medical Savings Accounts.[142]

In Alberta, a December 2001 report from the Premier's Advisory Council on Health headed by Deputy Prime Minister Don Mazankowski made 10 recommendations for reform, including reconfiguring the health system to encourage more choice and competition and diversifying revenues beyond the federal and provincial government.[143]

Policymakers are beginning to recognize what is wrong with a single-payer system. In a system in which health care at the point of service is free, the incentive facing the individual is to visit doctors often. The incentives for doctors, who are paid a government-set rate per visit, is to maximize patient visits. And the incentive facing politicians and those who manage the system is to invest in low-tech, primary care, which is just the sort that the majority of taxpayers are likely to use in any given year.

Like the United States, Canada would benefit from the flourishing of Medical Savings Accounts (MSAs) or Health Savings Accounts (HSAs). Incentives, again, are universal and MSAs and HSAs get the incentives right. MSAs and HSAs put the insurance back in health insurance and provide individuals with an economic stake in choosing the most efficient way to consume health care services.

MSAs and HSAs face steep political odds in both Canada and the United States. It is true that health care is even more politicized and plays an even larger role in the identity of Canadians than it does in the United States. The good news is that MSAs and HSAs need not be as radical, or disruptive, of the public system as they might first appear.

Canadian doctor and author, David Gratzer, has done much thinking and writing on how to introduce MSAs and their healthy incentives into Canada. Unlike the United States, where the adoption of MSAs largely requires a tweaking of the tax and regulatory codes, in Canada they can be introduced as part of the public system.

"MSAs are themselves ideologically neutral," writes Gratzer. "If all private involvement in health care is deemed a bad idea—a view often proposed by Medicare's most ardent supporters—it would still be possible to have a government-run and government financed MSA system."[144]

Gratzer notes that there are three models from which Canadian policymakers could choose.

A public model, where the government provides the catastrophic insurance and taxpayer money funds the spending accounts. The amount deposited into the spending account could depend on the age, sex, and health condition of the individual, with those more likely to need more care receiving more money.

A private model, under which Canadians purchase the insurance from private insurance companies and fund the accounts out of their own pocket, albeit with possible mandatory contributions.

A mixed model, where the government could provide the insurance, but citizens would fund their accounts on their own, or vice-versa, or some other combination.

There is no inherent reason why public funding dictates the current single-payer system. "MSAs are in fact both a health policy and an income redistribution policy, something that should appeal to left-wing thinkers," note economists Fred McMahon and Martin Zelder. "General revenues will support MSAs, with an individual's MSA based on medical need, regardless of income. In fact, the idea behind MSAs might well be described as, 'From each according to ability, from each according to need.'"[145]

CONCLUSION:
An Appeal to Reason *and* Compassion

In both sections of this book, we have seen that for all the vaunted differences between the health care systems in the United States and Canada, they both suffer symptoms of the same disease—the disease of central control. The cure is to open both systems to competition and consumer choice.

The greatest risk to both systems is not that they will go bankrupt. It is that they will come to see human beings as nothing but cost centers. Both systems must keep faith with the purpose of health care, which is, after all, to serve people. Both must see each new patient cured as a cause for joy. If we allow ourselves to lose this concern, we will lose more than access, affordability, and quality in health care.

We will lose our humanity.

Notes to Part II

Introduction

1. Barbara Crossette, "Canada's Health Care Shows Strains," *New York Times*, October 11, 2001.

2. See, for example, Milton Friedman, "How to Cure Health Care," *Public Interest* (Winter 2001): 3-30.

Chapter One

3. David Gratzer, *Code Blue: Reviving Canada's Health Care System*, (Toronto: ECW Press, 1999), p. 182.

4. Michael E. Porter and Elizabeth Olmsted Teisberg, "Redefining Competition in Health Care," *Harvard Business Review* (June 2004): 65-76.

Chapter Two

5. Regina Herzlinger, "Prix-Fixe Rip-Off," *Wall Street Journal*, June 13, 2003.

Chapter Three

6. Forrest McDonald, *E Pluribus Unum: The Formation of the American Republic 1776-1790*, Liberty Fund, Indianapolis, 1979, p. 17.

7. Pat and Hugh Armstrong with Claudia Fegan, *Universal Health Care: What the United States Can Learn from the Canadian Health Experience* (New York: The New Press, 1998): 6.

8. Michael Rachlis and Carol Kushner, *Strong Medicine: How to Save Canada's Health Care System* (Toronto: Harper Collins, 1994), p. 219.

9. Rachlis and Kushner, *Strong Medicine*, p. 34. See also, William McArthur, Cynthia Ramsay, and Michael Walker, "Improving Health Care for Canadians," in McArthur, Ramsay, and Walker, eds., *Healthy Incentives: Canadian Health Reform in an International Context* (Vancouver: The Fraser Institute, 1996). Available digitally at *http://oldfraser.lexi.net/publications/books/health_reform/improving.html* (accessed July 30, 2004).

10. Rachlis and Kushner, *Strong Medicine*, p. 11.

11. Armstrong *et al.*, *Universal Health Care*, p. 19.

12. Gerard F. Anderson and Jean-Pierre Poullier, "Health Spending, Access, and Outcomes: Trends in Industrialized Countries," *Health Affairs*, Vol. 18, No. 3 (May/June 1999), Exhibit 5, p. 186.

13. Jane Fulton, *Canada's Health Care System: Bordering on the Possible* (Washington, D.C., Faulkner and Gray, 1993), p. 37.

14. Aaron Derfel, "Make Doctors Equal in Pay, Provinces Told," *National Post Online*, August 15, 2001.

15. Fulton, *Canada's Health Care System*, p. 82.

16. Rachlis and Kushner, *Strong Medicine*, p. 236.

Chapter Four

17. OECD Health Data 2004, First Edition, Table 10.

18. OECD Health Data, 2001.

19. Esmail and Walker, *How Good is Canadian Health Care?*; and a special data request for the author by The Fraser Institute.

20. Ian Bailey and Robert Benzie, "Premiers Threatened Health Coup: Provinces Could Set Their Own Standards of Care if Ottawa Doesn't Cough Up $7-Billion," *National Post Online*, August 4, 2001.

21. Jeffrey Simpson, "Saskatchewan's Big Health Care Bet," *The Globe and Mail*, December 18, 2001.

22. Mark Kennedy, "Health Care Will Eat 42% of Budgets, Report Says: Crisis Looming in 2020," *National Post Online*, October 20, 2001.

23. Bailey and Benzie, "Premiers Threatened Health Coup," August 4, 2001.

24. Fulton, *Canada's Health Care System*, p. 244.

25. Rachlis and Kushner, *Strong Medicine*, p. 217.

26. Fulton, *Canada's Health Care System*, p. 141.

27. Crossette, "Canada's Health Care Shows Strains," 2001.

Chapter Five

28. Quoted in David Gratzer, *Code Blue*, p. 48.

29. Gratzer, *Code Blue*, p. 19.

30. Sheryl Ubelacker, "Microbe Blamed for 100 Deaths at Quebec Hospital," Canadian Press, August 4, 2004.

31. Lysiane Gagnon, "Why Hospitals Make Me Sick," *The Globe and Mail*, August 9, 2004.

32. David Spurgeon, "Women Sue over Delays in Treatment for Breast Cancer," *British Medical Journal*, March 20, 2004.

33. Tom Blackwell, "Put Moratorium on Hospital Bed Closings, Coroner's Jury Demands: Hospital Overcrowding 'Critical' in Ontario, Inquest Found." *Ottawa Citizen*, November 18, 2000.

34. Dave Brown, "Suffering Patients Demand Answers," *Ottawa Citizen*, October 24, 2000.

35. Sharon Kirkey and L. Robert Morris, "'Suffering' Thousands Wait Seven Months for an MRI," *Ottawa Citizen*, January 22, 2001.

36. Kirkey and Morris, "'Suffering' Thousands Wait Seven Months for an MRI," January 22, 2001.

37. Brown, "Suffering Patients Demand Answers," October 24, 2000.

38. Vanessa Lu, "Private Clinic Called Tory 'Wedge,'" *Toronto Star*, July 29, 2001.

39. Louise Elliot, "Ontario Pays Family $150,000 for Drug-addicted Teen's US Treatment," *National Post Online*, December 21, 2001.

40. Marko Simunovic *et al.*, "A Snapshot of Waiting Times for Cancer Surgery Provided by Surgeons Affiliated with Regional Cancer Centers in Ontario," *Canadian Medical Association Journal* 165(4), (2001): 421-5.

41. Nadeem Esmail and Michael Walker, *Waiting Your Turn: Hospital Waiting Lists in Canada (13th edition)*, Vancouver: The Fraser Institute, October 2003.

42. Armstrong *et al.*, *Universal Health Care*, p. 56.

43. Armstrong *et al.*, *Universal Health Care*, p. 122.

44. Fulton, *Canada's Health Care System*, p. 37.

45. Quoted in Robert Benzie, "Health revolution spreads to Ontario," *National Post Online*, January 10, 2002.

46. Theresa Boyle, "Access to MRIs Varies Widely Among Patients," *Toronto Star*, November 15, 2000.

47. David Gamble, "Sparks Fly Over Royal Surgery in City," *Gazette*, May 2, 2000.

48. "Quebec Vows to Block Planned X-ray User Fees," *Gazette*, July 27, 2001.

49. OECD Health Data, 2003.

50. Tom Arnold, "X-Ray Labs Dangerously Outdated," *National Post*, October 12, 2000.

51. Quoted in Heather Sokoloff, "PET Scans Crucial for Finding Breast Cancer, Study Says," *National Post*, September 4, 2001.

52. Quoted in Sokoloff, "PET Scans Crucial," September 4, 2001.

53. Rachlis and Kushner, *Strong Medicine*, p. 199.

54. R.G. Evans *et al.*, "Controlling Health Expenditures—the Canadian Reality," *New England Journal of Medicine*, March 2, 1989, 320(9): 571-577.

55. Quoted in Simpson, *Star Spangled Canadians*, p. 207.

56. Quoted in Simpson, *Star Spangled Canadians*, pp. 203-204.

57. Quoted in Simpson, *Star Spangled Canadians*, pp. 203-204.

58. Quoted in Robert Sheppard, "We Are Canadian," *Maclean's*, December 25, 2000/January 1, 2001, p. 26.

59. Simpson, *Star Spangled Canadians*, pp. 201-202.

Chapter Six

60. Martin Zelder, "Canadian Health Reformers Should Understand RAND," *Fraser Forum* (February 2000): 8-10.

61. Martin Zelder, "The Ultimate Health Care Reform," *Fraser Forum* (February 2000): 15-16.

62. Zelder, "The Ultimate Health Care Reform," February 2000, p. 16.

Chapter Seven

63. Robert Pear, "Michigan Senator Who Ran on Drug Issue will Lead Democrats in Debate," *New York Times*, July 15, 2002.

64. John R. Graham, *The Fantasy of Reference Pricing and the Promise of Choice in BC's Pharmacare*, Public Policy Sources no. 66 (Vancouver: The Fraser Institute, November 2002).

65. Devidas Menon, "Pharmaceutical Cost Control in Canada: Does It Work?" *Health Affairs* vol. 20, no. 3 (May/June 2001): 96.

66. Patricia M. Danzon, "Making Sense of Drug Prices," *Regulation*, vol. 23, no. 1, pp. 56-63.

67. John R. Graham, *Prescription Drug Prices in Canada and the United States—Part 2: Why the Difference?* Public Policy Sources no. 43 (Vancouver: The Fraser Institute, September 2000), p. 3.

68. Menon, "Pharmaceutical Cost Control in Canada: Does It Work?" 2001.

69. "Price Reduction for Humalog," Canadian Corporate Newswire, April 29, 1998.

70. Menon, "Pharmaceutical Cost Control in Canada: Does It Work?" 2001, p. 101.

71. William McArthur, "Prescription Drug Costs: Has Canada Found the Answer?" *National Center for Policy Analysis*, Brief Analysis no. 323, May 19, 2000.

72. McArthur, "Prescription Drug Costs: Has Canada Found the Answer?" May 19, 2000.

73. McArthur, "Prescription Drug Costs: Has Canada Found the Answer?" May 19, 2000.

74. John R. Graham, *The Fantasy of Reference Pricing*, November 2002.

75. Palmer D'Angelo Consulting, Inc., "Generic Drug Prices: A Canada US Comparison," PDCI Report Series, August 2002. Available digitally at *http://www.pdci.on.ca/pdf/Generic%20Pricing%20Study%20Final%20Report.pdf* (accessed June 9, 2003).

76. Ira Carnahan, "The Cheap Drugs Myth," *Forbes*, February 3, 2003.

77. Steven G. Morgan *et al.*, "Whither Seniors' Pharmacare: Lessons From (and for) Canada," *Health Affairs* vol. 22, no. 3 (May/June 2003): 49-59.

78. Morgan *et al.*, "Whither Seniors' Pharmacare," (May/June 2003).

79. John R. Graham, *Prescription Drug Prices in Canada and the United States—Part 3: Retail Price Distribution*, Public Policy Sources, no. 50 (Vancouver: The Fraser Institute, August 2001).

80. Graham, *Prescription Drug Prices in Canada and the United States—Part 2: Why the Difference*, September 2000, p. 3.

81. Graham, *Prescription Drug Prices in Canada and the United States—Part 2: Why the Difference*, September 2000, p. 10.

82. See *www.opensecrets.org*, a database of all US campaign contributions.

83. Richard L. Manning, "Products Liability and Prescription Drug Prices in Canada and the United States," *Journal of Law and Economics* 40 (April 1997): 203–243.

84. CMR International, *Market Access for New Medicines: Are Companies Changing Strategies?* R&D Briefing, no. 33, February 2001.

85. Menon, "Pharmaceutical Cost Control in Canada: Does It Work?" p. 100.

86. "Sure, Cheap Canadian Drugs," *Wall Street Journal*, July 23, 2002.

Chapter Eight

87. Merrill Matthews, Jr., "On a Bus to Bangor, Canadians Seeking Health Care," *Wall Street Journal*, July 5, 2002.

88. Romanow, *Building on Values: The Future of Health Care in Canada*, 2002; and Centers for Medicare and Medicaid Services, "The Nation's Health Dollar: 2001, Where It Went." Available digitally at *http://www.cms.hhs.gov/statistics/nhe/historical/chart.asp*.

89. Ira Carnahan, "The Cheap Drugs Myth," *Forbes*, February 3, 2003.

90. Graham, *Prescription Drug Prices in Canada and the United States—Part 2: Why the Difference*, September 2000, pp. 12-14.

Chapter Nine

91. Lisa Priest, "Private Labs Fill Growing Health Niche," *Globe and Mail*, December 29, 2001.

92. Vanessa Lu, "Saving Medicare from the Grassroots Up," *Toronto Star*, August 25, 2001.

93. Calgary Regional Health Authority, "11,000 more MRIs added to ease wait lists," News Release, May 4, 2000.

Chapter Ten

94. Ontario Hospital Association, *Building a Foundation for e-Health in Ontario: A Pathway to Improved Health Outcomes*, May 2001, p. 4.

95. Jocelyne Picot, *Telemedicine and Telehealth in Canada: A Selection of Projects*, World Telemedicine Congress (Toulouse, France), March 22, 2000.

96. John C. Hogenbirk, Raymond W. Pong, and Linda J. Liboiron, *Fee-for-service Reimbursement of Telemedicine Services in Canada, 1999/2000*, Centre for Rural and Northern Health Research, Laurentian University (April 2001).

97. Hogenbirk et al., *Fee-for-service Reimbursement of Telemedicine Services in Canada, 1999/2000*, 2001, p. 16.

98. Ontario Hospital Association, *Building a Foundation for e-Health in Ontario*, 2001, p. ii.

99. Canadian doctor who spoke with the author and requested anonymity.

100. Gratzer, *Code Blue*, p. 29.

101. Jean Roch Lafrance, "Ignore the 'Experts': Our Health Care System is in Crisis," *Ottawa Citizen*, January 29, 2001.

102. Dave Brown, "Tipping the System Back from the Brink," *Ottawa Citizen*, December 21, 2000.

Chapter Eleven

103. April Lindgren, "Ontario First Province in Canada to Ask Private Sector to Build, Maintain Hospital," *Ottawa Citizen*, December 1, 2001.

104. Lindgren, "Ontario First Province in Canada to Ask Private Sector to Build, Maintain Hospital," 2001.

105. Lindgren, "Ontario First Province in Canada to Ask Private Sector to Build, Maintain Hospital," 2001.

106. Lindgren, "Ontario First Province in Canada to Ask Private Sector to Build, Maintain Hospital," 2001.

107. Kelly Toughill, "Money Talks at Nova Scotia Clinic," *Toronto Star*, August 31, 2002.

108. Jill Mahoney, "Private Clinics Set to Open," *Globe and Mail*, December 1, 2000.

109. Brian Bergman, "The Alberta Test," *Maclean's*, April 3, 2000.

110. Dawn Walton, "Alberta Body OKs Overnight Clinics," *Globe and Mail*, February 9, 2002.

111. Mark Kennedy, "Ottawa to Examine Privatization," *National Post Online*, December 1, 2001.

112. Interview with PET Scan International, June 25, 2002.

113. Tom Arnold, "PET Scans to be Available—for $2,500: Private Firm to Offer Effective Cancer Test," *National Post*, July 9, 2001.

114. Arnold, "PET Scans to be Available," July 9, 2001.

115. Interview with Gabriela Perez, Best Doctors, July 2, 2002.

116. See *http://www.bestdoctors.com/en/default.htm*.

Chapter Twelve

117. Ross Finnie, *The Brain Drain: Myth and Reality—What It Is and What Should be Done*, Queen's University School of Policy Studies, Working Paper 13, January 2001.

118. Finnie, *The Brain Drain: Myth and Reality—What It Is and What Should be Done*.

119. Simpson, *Star Spangled Canadians*, p. 202.

120. Simpson, *Star Spangled Canadians*, p. 202.

121. Canada News Wire, "Rogers Media Releases Health Care Survey Results," November 5, 2001.

122. Lafrance, "Ignore the 'Experts,'" 2001.

123. Canadian Association of Radiologists, "Radiologists Work after Failing Exams with Obsolete Equipment: A Real Crisis." Available digitally at: *www.car.ca*.

124. Odile Nelson, "Devastating Doctor Shortage Leaves Patients without Family GP," *National Post*, October 25, 2001.

125. Aaron Derfel, "Make Doctors Equal in Pay, Provinces Told, The Rich Are Taking from the Poor, President-elect Says," *The National Post*, August 15, 2001.

126. Derfel, "Make Doctors Equal in Pay," August 15, 2001.

127. Lorne Tyrrell and Dale Dauphinee, *Task Force on Physician Supply in Canada*, prepared for the Canadian Medical Forum Task Force, November 22, 1999.

128. Robert Walker, "CRHA Says City is Short 200 Doctors," *Calgary Herald*, November 9, 2000.

Chapter Thirteen

129. Roy Romanow, "Executive Summary," *Final Report, Commission on the Future of Health Care in Canada* (November 2002), p. xxiii.

130. Roy Romanow, "Sustaining Medicare," *Final Report, Commission on the Future of Health Care in Canada* (November 2002), p. 2.

131. Tom Cohen, "Canada Gets Nod to Expand Health System," *Charleston Gazette*, November 29, 2002.

132. Randall Palmer, "Canada to Add Funds, Expand Health System," *Reuters Health*, February 6, 2003.

133. "Passing round the medicine hat," *The Economist*, February 8, 2003.

134. Quoted in Crossette, "Canada's Health Care Shows Strains," 2001.

135. Romanow, *Final Report*, Chapter 6.

136. Romanow, *Final Report*, Chapter 6.

137. Romanow, "Building on Values: The Future of Health Care in Canada," *Final Report*, p. 203.

138. Romanow, "Building on Values," *Final Report*, p. 204.

139. Keith Leslie, "McGuinty 'Puzzled' by Romanow's 'Defeatist' Take on National Pharmacare Plan," Canadian Press, August 7, 2004.

Chapter Fourteen

140. Quoted in Gratzer, *Code Blue*, pp. 46-47.

141. David Gratzer, "Double Eggs and Ham from Kirby," *National Post*, April 22, 2002.

142. David Gratzer, "We Need Choice and Competition," *National Post*, May 9, 2002.

143. Government of Alberta, *A Framework for Reform: Report of the Premier's Advisory Council on Health*, December 2001. Available digitally at *http://www.gov.ab.ca/home/health_first/documents_maz_report.cfm* (accessed April 3, 2003).

144. David Gratzer, ed., *Better Medicine: Reforming Canadian Health Care* (Toronto: ECW Press, 2002), p. 303.

145. Fred McMahon and Martin Zelder, *Making Health Spending Work*, Public Policy Sources no. 54 (Vancouver: The Fraser Institute, February 2000), p. 15.

About the Pacific Research Institute

The Pacific Research Institute champions freedom, opportunity, and personal responsibility for all individuals by advancing free-market policy solutions. It provides practical solutions for the policy issues that impact the daily lives of all Americans. And it demonstrates why the free market is more effective than the government at providing the important results we all seek—good schools, quality health care, a clean environment, and economic growth.

Founded in 1979 and based in San Francisco, PRI is a non-profit, non-partisan organization supported by private contributions. Its activities include publications, public events, media commentary, community leadership, legislative testimony, and academic outreach.

Health Care Studies

PRI demonstrates why a single-payer, Canadian model would be detrimental to the health care of all Americans. It proposes market-based reforms that would improve affordability, access, quality, and consumer choice.

Education Studies

PRI works to restore to all parents the basic right to choose the best educational opportunities for their children. Through research and grassroots outreach, PRI promotes parental choice in education, high academic standards, teacher quality, charter schools, and school finance reform.

Business and Economic Studies

PRI shows how the entrepreneurial spirit—the engine of economic growth and opportunity—is stifled by onerous taxes and regulations. It advances policy reforms that promote a robust economy, consumer choice, and innovation.

Technology Studies

PRI advances policies to defend individual liberty, foster high-tech growth and innovation, and limit regulation.

Environmental Studies

PRI reveals the dramatic and long-term trend towards a cleaner, healthier environment. It also examines and promotes the essential ingredients for abundant resources and environmental quality property rights, markets, local action, and private initiative.

About the Fraser Institute

The Fraser Institute is an independent Canadian economic and social research and educational organization. It has as its objective the redirection of public attention to the role of competitive markets in providing for the well-being of Canadians. Where markets work, the Institute's interest lies in trying to discover prospects for improvement. Where markets do not work, its interest lies in finding the reasons. Where competitive markets have been replaced by government control, the interest of the Institute lies in documenting objectively the nature of the improvement or deterioration resulting from government intervention. The work of the Institute is assisted by an Editorial Advisory Board of internationally-renowned economists. The Fraser Institute is a national, federally chartered non-profit organization financed by the sale of its publications and the tax-deductible contributions of its members, foundations, and other supporters.